PHYSICAL SCIENCE:

IT'S STRUCTURE AND DEVELOPMENT

SELECTED CHAPTERS

EDWIN KEMBLE

HOUGHTON MIFFLIN COMPANY

BOSTON   NEW YORK

Custom Publishing Editor: Lauri Coulter
Custom Publishing Production Manager: Kathleen McCourt
Project Coordinator: Andrea Wagner

Cover Design: Emily Quillen
Cover Photo: PhotoDisc

This book contains select works from existing Houghton Mifflin Company resources and was produced by Houghton Mifflin Custom Publishing for collegiate use. As such, those adopting and/or contributing to this work are responsible for editorial content, accuracy, continuity and completeness.

ISBN: 0-618-43015-6
N02773

1 2 3 4 5 6 7 8 9 – CCI – 05 04 03

Houghton Mifflin
Custom Publishing

222 Berkeley Street • Boston, MA 02116

Address all correspondence and order information to the above address.

Contents

Preface

This introduction to physical science is published as a contribution to the literature of general education. The two volumes are a radical revision of mimeographed notes prepared for an introductory course formerly given by the author in collaboration with Professor Gerald Holton as part of the Harvard College program in general education. The book was planned as a text for nonscience majors in liberal-arts colleges, but it is my hope that it may be of interest also to mature general readers and to teachers of introductory science in secondary schools.

The book combines an account of the fundamental concepts and principles of physical science with sketches of the history of the subject from its Greek beginnings to World War II. It is neither a systematic account of the achievements of physical science nor a history of the subject, but a personal response to the question, "What instruction in that field should be given today to college students who do not plan to enter scientific careers?"

Special education makes specialists. It provides the student with the knowledge and skills needed for a specific vocation. Its goal is definite; its educational program need not look to the left or right as it moves toward that goal. General education, however, has no such narrow focus. It is education independent of vocational bias for all who wish to understand the world they live in. The purpose of general education is to enlarge the mind and develop the critical faculties. It seeks to prepare the student to share in the intellectual life of his time and to cope with the problems that will confront him as a responsible member of society.

Clearly, any specific plan for general education that makes sense for today must take account of the profound social and political changes now in progress throughout the world. In 1945 a special committee of the Harvard faculty, appointed to study the objectives of general education in a free society, took the position that the central problem of nonvocational education should be to reconcile the sense of pattern and direction, which our society inherits from the past, with the need for experimentation, innovation, and adjustment pressed upon us by the advances in science and the march of events.[1] In the precarious world of today this judgment still seems to go to the heart of the matter.

Americans like to meet their problems on a day-to-day basis and are inclined to let the future of society take care of itself. But in recent years there has been a growing realization that the time for such an attitude has come to an end—that the possibility of avoiding the vast new hazards that face mankind depends on a widespread readjustment of our inherited assumptions, purposes, and practices. The swift pace of technological change and the world-wide population explosion make it certain that the future will be very different from the past. There is all too little time in which to prepare for it. Many of us believe that a continuous reappraisal of the presuppositions on which our society is based is a necessary condition for our cultural survival. Equally necessary is the thoughtful scrutiny of new conceptions and social proposals, lest we commit ourselves prematurely to views whose ultimate consequences we have failed to foresee. Reappraisal and scrutiny *are* the order of the day among those who take interest in the world in preparation for their children and grandchildren—especially in our universities and liberal-arts colleges, where young men and women wrestle with academic courses and wonder what they all add up to. In designing a general education program we do well to bear in mind the bewildering nature of the problem faced by the thoughtful undergraduate. In a world beset with anxieties, flooded with half-digested knowledge, dissatisfied with the old answers and uncertain of the new, he must make up his mind what is true, what is important, and where he is to stand. His problem is emotional as well as intellectual. It is synthetic as well as analytic.

In these circumstances the conscientious college teacher devising an introductory science course for nonscientists has a difficult assignment. All agree that basic instruction in science is an essential part of general education. The world of the space age cannot be understood without some scientific background. But to say that the most important task of general education has to do with the adjustment of social tradition to the need for social innovation is to relegate the teaching of physical science to a minor place or suggest a new interpretation of what the teaching of science is to involve. In the past, courses in the physical sciences have been organized around such important, but strictly technical, topics as Newton's laws of motion, thermodynamics, optics, the periodic table, and the law of mass action. Those topics must continue to occupy the center of the stage, but the 1945 Harvard committee proposed a change of emphasis in science courses intended for general education—a change designed to bring out the relevance of science to social tradition and social change. Specifically, the suggestion was that greatly increased attention be given to the history of science and to the relation between the growth of scientific knowledge and other aspects of the history of our culture. They argued, in other words, for a fuller recognition of the fact

---

[1] The committee, headed by the Dean of the Faculty of Arts and Sciences, Paul H. Buck, was appointed by President James B. Conant in the middle of World War II. Its report was published by Harvard University in 1945 under the title *General Education in a Free Society*.

that science is a human activity as well as a body of organized knowledge. Their proposal won widespread approval and achieved an observable effect on many campuses.

Any attempt to put such a plan into practice is bound, of course, to run into practical difficulties. It takes time and textbook space to deal with new matter, and it is not easy to push aside or compress the treatment of the traditional technical topics. High on the list of social objectives for general education should be the improvement of channels of communication between different elements in society, especially between scientists and nonscientists. From this point of view it is essential that nonscientists learn something of the elementary vocabulary of the scientist—a vocabulary inseparable from the basic principles of science itself. Only by direct instruction in the elements of technical science can this need be met. Moreover, recent advances in science must be included in the list of topics discussed in a general education course. Students are eager to hear about the scientific items that find their way into the newspapers—about lasers and quasars, multibillion-volt particle accelerators, and violations of the parity principle, to mention only a few. The teacher-scientist is under severe psychological compulsion to bring his course up to date by including just such items. In them his own interest is normally centered. So the technical subject matter of science, like a gas, expands to fill all the available space. The achievements of Galileo, Isaac Newton, Thomas Young, Lavoisier, Carnot, and Faraday seem to be "old hat." Does it really make sense in a terminating elementary college course in physical science to take time for these scientific worthies of the past? The schedule is crowded and the history of science lies outside the competence of the average instructor. Why not leave the history, sociology, and philosophy of science to the departments of history, sociology, and philosophy?

To this proper question there can be no unambiguous answer. My own response is that I have tried the procedure recommended by the Harvard committee and am convinced of its merits. In my experience it is a workable procedure that fits the changing educational needs of our time. I note that the issues of our day—war and peace, racial injustice, overpopulation, automation, the pollution and contamination of the atmosphere and water supply, the breakdown of traditional values—are all issues calling for concerted and imaginative action by large segments of society, if not by the entire world community. They are all connected with the changing relation between the individual and society, as technology becomes more sophisticated and population densities rise. If our universities and colleges are to prepare a generation of citizens capable of coping with such problems they can hardly be content to be no more than institutions for the accumulation and transmission of specialized knowledge treated as an end in itself. Should they not be, as many of them now are, centers in which conversations cutting across departmental lines are used to develop the wisdom and know-how needed for an era of swift social change? From this point of view at any rate, we need general educational courses that make use of the widest possible frame of reference and seek to make a modest contribution to the philosophy of the students who take them.

In practice such a policy can add appreciably to the meaning and interest of a course in physical science without undue sacrifice of technical scientific material. It does not require a large fraction of total class time to change the atmosphere of a program of study.

A major advantage in the historical approach comes from the fact that by taking up scientific concepts in the order of their historical development we begin with the study of phenomena with which nearly all students are familiar. Science is a search for regularity in nature; it seeks to formulate the precise laws which describe phenomena that are repeated or can be repeated under controlled conditions. The first physical phenomena to yield to this search had to do with the simpler aspects of everyday experience: the motion of the heavenly bodies as they sweep across the sky, the motion of falling bodies and projectiles, the composition of forces, the expansion of gases under reduced pressure, and the flow of heat. Such phenomena can be studied with simple measuring instruments and analyzed with a minimum of mathematical machinery. The scientific rules governing them are easily understood, because they appeal to the beginner as little more than a codification of his own direct experience and common sense. In beginning our account of physical science with such topics we easily establish the confidence of the student in his own ability to comprehend and minimize his dependence on the authority of others.

Furthermore, if we start with an examination of the historical beginnings of science, we take advantage of a well-established principle: the story of a developing activity carried on by people whose names are known is easier to follow and more interesting than the logical analysis of a body of knowledge. The historical procedure provides students with stimulating glimpses into the "thickets of erroneous observations, misleading generalizations, inadequate formulations, and unconscious prejudice"[2] through which the first scientists fought their way from one key position to another. The nature and significance of the scientific enterprise are revealed in part by a study of its achievements, but more fully by a study of the story of its development. The student who hears the story is likely to shed some of the naïve disdain for the past and the excessive devotion to the up-to-date so common among young people in a time of revolutionary change. He learns not only *what* the scientists have found out about the physical universe, but also *how* they found it out. He discovers why it took so long to devise the conceptual structure on which our present understanding of that universe rests. In short, the historical approach to the study of physical science opens up a new dynamical dimension of meaning worth all it costs.

Admittedly, the introduction of fringe areas of history, philosophy, and sociology into a rigorous course in physical science does complicate the ever-present problem of time. The usual time allotment for such a course is no more than that appropriate to a one-year four-credit-hour educational unit. It will be evident that

---

[2] James B. Conant, *On Understanding Science*, New Haven, Yale University Press, 1947.

the selection of scientific topics to be dealt with must be made with a parsimonious eye. Any attempt to be fair to the departments of astronomy, chemistry, geology, and physics by giving them equal representation is out at the start! Many faculties and teachers have preferred to handle the ticklish question of relative priorities by allowing each department in the area of physical science to work out its own version of humanized science for nonscientists. The obvious advantages of this procedure require no comment here. Suffice it to note that when we ask the questions "How?" and "Why?," with reference to the successive stages in the progress of any one of the physical sciences, we are forced to consider the progress of the others. From our point of view a historical introduction to one science that leaves the others out would be unthinkable. Therefore this textbook, despite its dominant emphasis on physics, is labeled "physical science." The emphasis itself rests primarily on the fact that, despite its enormous debt to astronomy and chemistry, physics is clearly the central discipline which unifies the physical sciences. The original plan for Harvard's general education program called for courses in physical science to be "built around a core of physics." As a physicist teaching one of the courses based on that plan, I was not tempted to disregard the injunction.

Our original course program included a short series of lectures on the fundamentals of geology and an annual geological field trip —all much enjoyed by the class. The subject is appealing and could make a useful connecting link between the physical and biological sciences. Nevertheless, it lies somewhat to one side of the primary objectives of the present work. For that reason, and to reduce the size of an overbulky manuscript, I have regretfully omitted the original chapter on geological processes.

Every introductory textbook in physical science must take some account of the interactions between science and technology. The beginnings of science can be traced to primitive technology; public support of science today rests on confidence in the value of its technological applications. Chapter 15 deals at some length with the history of the relation of steam-engine technology to thermodynamics. On the other hand, limitations of space have made it necessary to focus attention primarily on the essential facts, concepts, and principles of pure science—to the exclusion of many topics of much technological value that are not essential to an appreciation of the conceptual outlook of the contemporary physicist, chemist, and astronomer.

Volume 1 follows in the main the line of a single historical sequence of developments: the rise of geometric astronomy, culminating in the Copernician revolution, the formulation of Newtonian mechanics, and the applications of Newton's theory to planetary motion, elasticity, energy, thermodynamics, and kinetic theory. The final chapter on the kinetic-molecular theory of heat introduces the problem of the structure of matter and brings out the limitations of Newton's mechanics when applied to the motion of atoms and molecules. In Chap. 5 the chronological order is interrupted to round out the story of geometric astronomy. It contains an account of the successive stages by which measurements of the trigonometric parallax values of nearby stars have been used to evaluate the distances of the external galaxies and to give estimates of the Hubble age of the galactic universe.

Volume 2 continues the story of the evolution of our ideas about the structure of matter. My primary goal in writing that volume has been to give the reader an honest and intelligible account of the upheaval that quantum theory and relativity theory brought to physics and chemistry in the early decades of the twentieth century. This revolutionary upheaval provides the history of physical science with a dramatic climax. It transformed and unified the various branches of physical science, eliminating the dividing lines between mechanics, electromagnetism, optics, chemistry, and astronomy. It opened up the road to a much deeper and more detailed understanding of physical phenomena than the scientists of the nineteenth century ever dreamed of. We have yet to learn what to do with the new capacity to control natural forces made available to mankind by this sudden access of new knowledge. Moreover, the story has a certain bearing on the cultural problem of innovation and tradition to which our conception of general education has been tied. The scientists who participated in the great revolution in the early twentieth century had to face, in an acute form, the need to reconcile inherited patterns of thought with new facts and conditions. The crisis has been surmounted, but in the 1920's very few of the older scientists were able to free themselves sufficiently from ingrained habits of thought to make important contributions to the new theory. Accordingly, despite the notorious difficulty of explaining the quantum theory and relativity theory to students and readers of limited mathematical background, I have chosen to focus the second volume of this book on the revolution generated by those theories.

The new physics and the new chemistry have their roots in the physics and chemistry of the nineteenth century. In addition to the development of classical mechanics and its application to the kinetic molecular theory of heat described in Volume 1, these roots include the classical atomic formulation of chemical theory achieved by Dalton, Avogadro, Cannizzaro, and Mendeleev, classical electromagnetism, and classical optics. Nine chapters in the second volume are devoted to the elements of these branches of prequantum-physical science and to such transition topics as the discovery of the atomic nature of electrical charge, the mass spectrograph, the properties of X rays, and natural radioactivity. Five chapters are devoted to quantum theory and relativity.

To summarize: This book is intended to help the liberal-arts student or general reader to gain a balanced understanding of the nature and significance of physical science. Because physical science is both a complex social activity and a complex fund of knowledge, the book is a mixture of diverse ingredients involving numerous changes of pace. Sections having to do with the history of science, its methods, and its contributions to philosophy should be relatively easy to follow, whereas other sections dealing with the concepts and mathematical structure of physical theory are necessarily more difficult. The more qualitative parts, I hope, will allow the average reader to catch his breath between sections containing an appreciable amount of mathematical detail, but I have not side-stepped basic principles because they may make some demand on the ability of the reader to follow close reasoning or bits of simple mathematics.

The book makes demands on the instructor as well as on the student. The work as a whole is not too large for an interested student to read from cover to cover during an academic year, but it does contain more material than the average student can easily digest in a normal one-year course. Hence, the use of the two volumes as a textbook places on the instructor the responsibility for choosing what is to be covered carefully, what is to be skimmed, and what is to be left out. In my own classes I have made numerous omissions. Any excisions create gaps in the logical structure of the course, but such gaps should be less serious when the student, by examining his textbook, can see what has been omitted.

Many students from our better secondary schools enter college today with a background in elementary calculus and sound physics, but others of equal intelligence, who do not look forward to scientific careers, lack that kind of training. I assume that most readers of this book will belong to the latter class. On that premise, I have defined all but the most elementary mathematical terms as they are introduced and have used the simplest possible mathematical terminology in the discussion of physical laws. Ultimately, however, any serious attempt to formulate the fundamental laws must make use of the beginnings of differential and integral calculus. The required mathematical concepts have become an indispensable part of the subject matter. Hence, the text and the appendices include as much mathematical instruction as seems necessary for an understanding of each physical topic. On the other hand, I have not considered the development of skill in the mathematical solution of physical problems to be a basic objective science course addressed to nonscientists.

It may be well to mention here the important part that collateral reading and the writing of essays played in the work of the course on which this text is based. During the year each student was expected to write four or five rather lengthy papers dealing with or stemming from collateral reading. A good deal of latitude was allowed in the selection of specific topics appropriate to the course. The staff took pains in guidance and in detailed criticism of the essays in order to encourage a creative and thoughtful response to the reading. As a result, the essay feature of our course plan proved more successful than we could have anticipated. The papers submitted were surprisingly mature. Inasmuch as the parallel science courses in the Harvard general education program made use of the same feature, President Conant instituted an annual prize competition for the best essays. Exchanges between staff and students provoked by the critical examination of each paper provided a feedback mechanism helpful to both. Such an essay program creates work for the instructional staff, but it can pay off in intellectual stimulus and development.

This book claims no fundamental originality of conception. Its broad objectives are similar to those embodied in the excellent textbooks of Professor Holton[3] and Professor Rogers.[4] As a matter of fact the present work may be described as a late-blooming product of a general concern over the tactics of teaching science to nonscientists that developed among physics and chemistry teachers in the northeastern section of our country during the early postwar years. At that time Professor Rogers and I were fellow enthusiasts and friends of long standing. As he generously explains in the preface to his text, we shared ideas concerning this mutual interest with complete freedom at every opportunity—and there were many of them. I take satisfaction in recording here my debt to him for these stimulating exchanges in the period when our respective plans were still in the formative stage. Professor Holton and I were collaborators in teaching almost continuously from his arrival in Cambridge, in 1943, until my retirement. We have shared the same interests and fought the same battles. His imaginative advice, helpful criticism, and continuous support have had much to do with the shaping of this text. In the circumstances some points of resemblance between what I have set down and the textbooks of Rogers and Holton are inevitable and at the same time coincidental—I have not studied to avoid them.

It may not be out of place to mention at this point the fact that my espousal of the cause of general education in 1945 meant a radical shift of commitment. For more than twenty years prior to World War II my research activity had been focused on the developing quantum theory. My teaching had been confined almost exclusively to upper-level courses in the various branches of mathematical physics. My knowledge of the history of science and of chemistry and astronomy was limited. To develop a course or write a book attempting to weave together material from these fields adjacent to physics meant that I must acquire some additional general education for myself. It involved sticking my neck out a long way. I chose to run the risk because the problem fascinated me and because I was convinced of its importance. Fortunately, I could draw freely on the wisdom of a notable group of stimulating colleagues engaged in parallel enterprises in the same general education program: I. Bernard Cohen, Thomas S. Kuhn, Philipe Le Corbeiller, Leonard K. Nash, and, in my own department, Gerald Holton. My memories of the regular lunch-time sessions devoted to discussion of our common interests in the history and philosophy of science are warm and lively. Every member of the group, in one way or another, has made a substantial contribution to my education and to this textbook.

Mention should be made as well of the influence of President Conant. It was his vigorous and far-seeing leadership that brought the Harvard general education program into being. Moreover, his wartime experience as Chairman of the National Defense Research Committee gave him a special point of view regarding

---

[3] Gerald Holton, *Introduction to Concepts and Theories in Physical Science*, Addison-Wesley Press, Inc., Cambridge, Mass., 1952; Gerald Holton and Duane H. D. Roller, *Foundations of Modern Physical Science*, Addison-Wesley Publishing Company, Inc., Reading, Mass., 1958.

[4] Eric M. Rogers, *Physics for the Inquiring Mind*, Princeton University Press, Princeton, N.J., 1960.

the teaching of science to nonscientists. His Terry lectures at Yale in 1946[2] reported many examples of the bewilderment of educated laymen in the discussion of war problems with scientists—bewilderment due not to lack of scientific knowledge or failure to understand technical jargon, but to a fundamental ignorance of what scientific research can and cannot do. He attributed this difficulty to a basic weakness in the scientific education of nonscientists in schools and colleges and called for a radical reform. Specifically, he proposed to set aside the usual objectives of the survey course in physical science in order to concentrate on a few historical examples of the development of science. Between 1946 and 1950 he personally directed a successful experimental course in physical science that was based on scientific case histories. The material collected by his staff for use in that course is an important addition to the literature of science teaching.[5] Although those of us in charge of the other three physical science courses in the initial general education program did not follow Conant all the way in his drastic proposal, all were influenced by his point of view and eager to make use of his case histories. Looking back I am keenly aware of my own obligation to Mr. Conant for the strong light he shed on the educational possibilities offered by detailed studies of specific episodes in the history of science.

So many different friends and acquaintances have responded at one time or another to my calls for assistance that to thank them here in an adequate manner is an impossible task. Among those who have generously made critical examination of one part or another of the manuscript are Professors Robert S. Cohen, David L. Anderson, Aaron J. Ihde, C. Alvarez-Tostado, John Hermann Randall, Henry Aiken, F. J. Rutherford, and Dr. Theodore J. Schulz. In working out the later sections of Chap. 5, dealing with the expanding universe of galaxies, I have had many helpful consultations with various members of the staffs of the Harvard College Observatory and the Smithsonian Astrophysical Observatory. Special thanks are due to Mr. Richard B. Rodman for the helpful hints which followed his scrutiny of that chapter. Those on whom I have called for advice carry no responsibility for the way in which their suggestions have been used, but I am most grateful for the help which I trust has kept me from going seriously astray.

The final revision of the manuscript for publication has been a two-man job made possible by the generous and efficient collaboration of Professor Edward P. Clancy of Mount Holyoke College. He has given freely of his time and enery; his teaching experience, keen critical sense, and unfailing good judgment have substantially improved the text and saved me from many pitfalls. My debt to him is a very large one.

By singular good fortune I showed the manuscript of this first volume to Mr. John H. Durston, of Educational Services, Inc., some time before it was ready for the publishers. He took an immediate interest and has acted as my editorial guide and mentor ever since. Through his kindly intervention and unique editorial

---

[5] Cf. *Harvard Case Histories in Experimental Science*, James Bryant Conant, general editor, Leonard K. Nash, associate editor, Harvard University Press, Cambridge, Mass., 1940; James Bryant Conant, *Science and Common Sense*, Yale University Press, New Haven, Conn., 1951.

craftsmanship miracles have been accomplished with my sometimes ragged prose. I hardly know how to thank him.

To the director and staff of the M.I.T. Press I am much beholden for their interest and continued encouragement as well as for the skills they have brought to bear on the publication process.

Finally, I wish to express my appreciation to the Alfred P. Sloan Foundation for a grant-in-aid without which it would not have been possible to finance the preparation and publication of this manuscript.

Cambridge, Massachusetts   EDWIN C. KEMBLE
April, 1966

CHAPTER I

The Greek Age in the History of Science

The main business of the preceding chapter was the description of the relatively simple geometrical facts of elementary astronomy and of the way in which these facts have been utilized in the construction of maps of the earth and the sky. With these facts in mind, and with an appropriate vocabulary for dealing with them, we are ready to turn back to the more complex and treacherous questions of early scientific history which were briefly introduced in Secs. 2 and 3 of Chap. 1.

Any attempt on the part of a scientist untrained in archaeology to sketch the outlines of the beginnings of science is of necessity a hazardous enterprise, for the history of early science is inextricably bound up with the whole vast and intricate story of ancient man. Nevertheless, it is necessary to touch upon these matters if we are to appreciate science as a social activity of long standing.

To establish a time scale let us begin with the age of the earth, believed to be about four to five billion years. Animals with hard shells became abundant about 500 million years ago. Gordon Childe[1] informs us that Neanderthal men, extinct cousins of *Homo sapiens*, were giving ceremonial burial to their dead and providing the graves with food and tools more than 100,000 years ago. The savagery of the cave men and hunters of the old Stone Age merged into the barbarism of the first settled agricultural communities perhaps 10,000 years ago. The first civilizations with cities, specialized craftsmen, and primitive forms of writing appeared in the valleys of the Tigris, Euphrates, Nile, and Indus rivers about 5000 to 6000 years ago. The decipherable story of civilization accordingly has occupied only one or two percent of the life of man as a fully differentiated biological species.

Since the history of science in the broader sense (Chap. 1, Sec. 2) includes the history of primitive technology, it goes back far beyond the first civilizations. Moreover, barbaric man's accumulation of practical knowledge was imposing, to say the least. It is to him, and not to civilized man, that we can trace the discovery of fire-making and cooking, the invention of weapons for hunting, the

1. Science Before the Greeks

---

[1] Gordon Childe, *What Happened in History* (Penguin Books, Ltd., Harmondsworth, England, 1942), p. 15. Cf. also G. E. Hutchinson, *American Scientist* **45**, 1957, p. 89.

discovery of edible plants, the development of agriculture, the domestication of animals, the art of pottery making, and the invention of a technology for shaping bronze tools and weapons. These achievements in physical and biological technology were accompanied by developments of another sort: the elaboration of language and the creation of myths of various kinds. Language is surely the greatest of inventions and perhaps the most striking characteristic of human life as distinguished from the life of the higher nonhuman animals. Its development opened the way to the invention of abstract ideas, to the formulation of questions regarding the why and how of the order of nature, and so to the creation of the myths by which these questions were first answered. Such myths and the ceremonies by which they are acted out play an essential role in the organization of the primitive societies that remain in the modern world. Archaeological research shows that in ancient times, as far back as records go, the routines of agriculture and the practical arts were interwoven with religious ceremonies and superstitious practices to form well-defined cultural patterns of behavior and thought.

We can be sure, on the basis of modern anthropological studies and of what we know of the records of earlier civilizations, that primitive cultural patterns in the stone ages and the copper age were of vast importance in the maintenance of the stability of tribal organizations. Anthropological studies emphasize the bizarre variety of social forms created by primitive cultures and also the strict limitations which each of these cultures imposed on the range of thought of those who participated in it. There can be no doubt that the rigidity and permanence of the thought patterns of the various tribes of ancient men must have restricted enormously the exploration of new techniques and new ideas. In fact, one cannot help wondering whether the major advances in the evolution of early society were not in nearly every case products of times of social stress due to changing climate, external aggression, the pressure of growing population, and the like. If "challenge and response" were of crucial importance for the growth and decay of civilizations, as Arnold Toynbee[2] has argued, they must have been equally significant in the life of savage and barbaric man.

To the author of these pages a chief impression gathered from the archaeological accounts of precivilized man is a sense of the magnitude of the achievements and the ingenuity which they demanded. The period of time required for the conversion of the earliest food-gathering cultures into urban civilizations was very great, but for most of this time the population density was extremely small. Moreover, these early people were divided into many tribal communities isolated from each other by geographic and language barriers. The rate of diffusion of new techniques must have been exceedingly low and the number of individuals effectively involved in the evolution of the practical arts at any one time correspondingly small. When, in addition, we remember the inhibiting action of rigid cultures on the discovery of new techniques, we must be struck by the intelligence with which early men met their problems

[2] Arnold J. Toynbee, *A Study of History,* abridged edition, D. C. Somervell, Ed. (Oxford University Press, New York, 1947), Chaps. V, VI, and VII.

in times of change and stress, when the influence of tradition was forced into the background. These considerations support the conclusion, indicated by the study of skulls, that the biological evolution of the brain of man was substantially complete well before the dawn of civilization, and perhaps as long as a million years ago.

But slowly and step by step our cultural ancestors in the Near East discovered techniques that opened the way to civilization. They learned the arts of drainage and irrigation by which fertile lowlands along the lower Euphrates, Tigris, and Nile could be converted into fields of abundant grain. They harnessed oxen and invented sailboats. They learned to make bricks, to convert copper ores into metallic copper by heating with charcoal, to mix tin with copper, and to cast and hammer the alloy into durable weapons and tools. Then about 3000 B.C. came an economic and social revolution in which self-sufficient villages were replaced by cities deeply involved in foreign trade and organized internally into a variety of specialized crafts and other occupations.

For a while adaptation to the new way of living brought with it relatively rapid advances in the art of writing, in mathematics, architecture, and technology. The great and precisely laid-out pyramids constructed in the Fourth Egyptian Dynasty, about 2500 B.C., bear extraordinary testimony to the technical achievements of the early civilizations that came with the development of cities. Unfortunately, however, these early civilizations in irrigated river valleys surrounded by arid regions were only too well adapted to what we today call "totalitarianism." The control of the annual floods of the Nile required a central organization, while the river itself, by providing a main highway through the kingdom, simplified the exercise of central authority. So Egypt became a stratified and monolithic state in which further progress was well-nigh impossible. Its civilization, protected from external invasion by its geographical location, achieved a remarkable stability, but it petrified in the process.

The Mesopotamian valley was the site of a succession of empires — the Sumerians, the Babylonians, the Assyrians, and the Persians ruled it in turn. The story of the cultural achievements of the Mesopotamian empires is still unfolding as the written records discovered by the archaeologists are gradually deciphered. Recent progress has led to a radical upward revision of our estimate of their attainments. In mathematics and astronomy they seem to have been well ahead of their Egyptian contemporaries when the Greeks first appeared on the shores of the eastern Mediterranean. Perhaps because of the struggles which accompanied shifts in power, the development of the arts of civilization continued in Mesopotamia long after it had virtually ceased in Egypt.

Nevertheless we must assume that in Mesopotamia as well as in Egypt the development of scientific conceptions was severely limited by the practical interests of the people and by their still primitive outlook on the universe.

It is difficult for us today to imagine the mythological and animistic universe in which these early peoples lived. The major physical phenomena were personalized. When the Nile failed to rise as expected, the Egyptians believed it was because the Nile *refused* to do so. There was no thought of the rainfall in the region of the headwaters. In those prescientific days men lacked our conception of impersonal natural law and our basic distinction between subjective knowledge (or appearance) and objective knowledge (tested fact free from individual bias). The significance of this fact is brought out in the following quotation:

> On this distinction [between subjective and objective], scientific thought has based a critical and analytical procedure by which it progressively reduces the individual phenomena to typical events subject to universal laws. Thus it creates an increasingly wide gulf between our perception of the phenomena (of nature) and the conceptions by which we make them comprehensible. We see the sun rise and set, but we think of the earth as moving round the sun. We see colors, but we describe them as wavelengths.... In the immediacy of primitive experience, however, there is no room for such a critical resolution of perceptions.[3]

So the distinction between subjective knowledge and objective knowledge, between appearance and reality, did not exist for primitive man. Dreams were not much less real than waking experiences. Symbols were identified with the things for which they stood. The Pharoahs of Egypt had pottery bowls inscribed with the names of their enemies. To quote again, "These bowls were solemnly smashed at a ritual ... ; and the object of this ritual was explicitly stated. It was that all of these enemies, obviously out of the Pharaoh's reach, should die."[4] It is no wonder the Egyptians and Babylonians did not progress in science beyond the immediately observed facts.

2. The Coming of the Greeks

So it was that the great advances in thought that laid the foundations of our western civilization came not from the empires of Mesopotamia and Egypt but from nomadic tribes that invaded the periphery of the eastern Mediterranean about the middle of the second millennium B.C. and for a period of time lived in conditions favorable to the free development of ideas. The Hebrews, who came into Palestine, were to replace the crude animistic and amoral religious cosmogonies of the great empires with the lofty conception of a creator who is the one great God of justice, mercy, and truth. The Hellenes, or Greeks, were to work out a critical approach to the understanding of the physical universe and the moral and social problems of mankind. Here we must restrict our consideration to the story of the Greeks.

The Greek-speaking Hellenic tribes were barbaric Aryans from the North who first invaded the Greek peninsula about 2000 B.C. Here they built up a rude civilization whose capital was Mycenae. About 1400 B.C. they conquered the Minoan kingdom on the island of Crete, and proceeded to assimilate much of its relatively advanced culture. At the end of the Bronze Age, however (about 1200 B.C.), they were themselves overwhelmed by a fresh wave of barbarian Hellenes. This second invasion seems to have resulted in

---

[3] H. and H. A. Frankfort, J. A. Wilson, T. Jacobsen, and W. A. Irwin, *The Intellectual Adventure of Ancient Man* (University of Chicago Press, Chicago, 1946), p. 11.

[4] H. and H. A. Frankfort *et al., op. cit.,* p. 13.

the destruction of nearly all that the Mycenaeans had built up. It threw the country into a period of anarchy in which the art of writing itself was lost. At about the same time, barbarian attacks and wars between the empires of Assyria, Babylonia, and Egypt plunged the whole Near East into chaos. According to Gordon Childe,[5] the civilized world passed through a period of darkness comparable to the Dark Ages in Europe some 1800 years later. He says of this era, "Not in a single state alone but over a large part of the civilized world history itself seems to be interrupted; the written sources dry up, the archaeological documents are poor and hard to date."

In Greece the time of darkness lasted for several hundred years. Then, in the time of Homer, came a renaissance, stimulated in large part by commercial contacts with the reviving cultures of Assyria, Babylon, Egypt, and Phoenicia. By 700 B.C. the new Greek civilization was pressing forward vigorously. As their population increased, the Greeks spread over the many islands of the Aegean Sea and secured a firm foothold on the shore of Asia Minor. From there the colonies spread westward to southern Italy and Sicily.

This new civilization contrasted in many ways with the great empires of Egypt and Babylon. It was broken up geographically by sea and mountains into islands, seacoasts, and tillable valleys. Politically it was for centuries an agglomeration of small city states torn by local rivalries and fatally weakened in the course of time by wars between Athens and Sparta. As their populations grew, these city states developed specialized economies and came to depend on the exchange of food products and manufactured articles in maritime trade.

Commercial rivalry led to the rapid improvement of their arts and crafts. The governmental organization went through many phases including monarchy, oligarchy, dictatorship, and a form of democracy based on slave labor. In the end all the Greek cities were overpowered by Philip II of Macedon and his son, Alexander the Great.

The Greeks had a tumultuous and brilliant history. They fought with one another, with the Persians, and with the Phoenicians. They created a magnificent architecture and sculpture whose remnants the world still reveres, and they developed political institutions that have continued to influence the political structure of the western world until today. Table 3.1 shows a brief list of important dates worth bearing in mind.

As creative thinkers and artists the Greeks were unsurpassed. They were observant travelers, speculative and for their time singularly unprejudiced. They developed a language that could deal with abstract conceptions. They valued ideas, talked much about them, and wrote books about them. To the Greeks we owe the idea of critical thinking and the creation of an intellectual life. Their contributions to art, moral philosophy, and science were all superlative. In the words of Bruno Snell, "They discovered the human mind."[6]

---

[5] Gordon Childe, op. cit., p. 185.

[6] Bruno Snell, The Discovery of the Mind (Harper and Row, Inc., New York, 1960).

Table 3.1   Chronology of Greek Science

4.6 billion years ago, earth's crust solidified
500 million years ago, hard-shelled animals appear
100,000 years ago, *Homo sapiens*; ceremonial burial of dead
4000 to 3000 B.C., early cities and primitive writing
2400 B.C. (approx.), Great Pyramid of Cheops
2000 B.C., first Greek invasion
1200 B.C., beginning of Dark Age
725 B.C., alphabet from Phoenicia
700–500 B.C., commercial expansion
492–479 B.C., successful war with Persia
460–429 B.C., Gold–Age of Pericles
404 B.C., fall of Athenian Empire
336–323 B.C., empire of Alexander
197–168 B.C., Roman conquest of eastern Mediterranean
A.D. 390, partial destruction of library at Alexandria

Thales, 640?–546 B.C.	Aristotle, 384–323 B.C.
Pythagoras, 582–506 B.C.	Euclid, 330–275 B.C.
Leucippus, 475 B.C.	Aristarchus, 310–250 B.C.
Philolaus, 450 B.C.	Apollonius of Perga, *fl.* 220 B.C.
Plato, 427–347 B.C.	Hipparchus, 190–120 B.C.
Eudoxus, 403–356 B.C.	Eratosthenes, *c.* 276–*c.* 194 B.C.
Heracleides, 388–315 B.C.	Ptolemy *fl.* A.D. 170

Modern anthropology tends to account for the differences in performance of people of different nations in terms of the conditions in which they live, both physical and cultural, rather than in terms of differences in biological brain capacity. So (at some risk of over-simplification) we may plausibly attribute the brilliant successes of the Greeks in art, philosophy, and science to the conditions in which they lived rather than to exceptional native ability. For example we note that the growth of a relatively democratic political organization among the Greeks brought with it a large degree of freedom of thought. Moreover, the Greeks came into contact with the technology and science of older civilizations without inheriting the rigid mythological and social conceptions of the earlier cultures. Greek education reached a high level, and the capitalistic commerce which developed in Greece induced an economic prosperity that permitted the formation of a leisure class from which an intellectual aristocracy could emerge. Thus these intellectual forbears of ours had many advantages over both their predecessors and their contemporaries in Egypt and in Mesopotamia.

3. Greek Contributions to Science

3.1. The story of the beginnings of Greek science is a part of the intellectual history of the Greeks, and their intellectual history is a part of the history of the development of the Greek "culture."[7] From the point of view of cultural anthropology there are several considerations that we do well to bear in mind. First, we should realize that differences in culture, such as those that exist today between the Bantus of Africa, the Chinese, and the Swiss, include not only differences in customs and social organization, in technology and religion, but differences in ways of thinking. The intel-

[7] Here we use the word "culture" in the anthropological sense as the total way of life of a people.

lectual component of a culture is its world of ideas, including its vocabulary and language structure, its habits of reasoning, the broad assumptions which its people habitually make, and the ways in which these are expressed in vocabulary and language structure. In the second place, we should realize that every thinking human mind gets its start in a particular culture — a particular inherited world of thought. Through education the child must enter into his intellectual inheritance, be it good or bad, before he can begin to think for himself. In the third place, we need to remind ourselves of the obvious fact that cultures are in a continuous process of evolution through experience. In this evolution religious, political, industrial, and intellectual leaders all play important parts. But whatever his sphere of activity, each leader must get his start in his own culture by working on the problems of his own time with the customs, organization, and mental equipment which that culture provides. Finally, we should appreciate the fact that, just as a tree trunk grows by the addition of successive layers of new wood overlaid on preceding layers, so a culture can only evolve by a continuous process from where it is. Each step forward or backward must be a step for which the historical process has made preparation.

So, if we are to discuss Greek science at all we should be thinking about what the Greek world in its day was ready for. In comparison with the science of the twentieth century, the science of the Greeks was very crude. On the other hand, the realization of this crudity is no excuse for an attitude of superiority on our part. It is no reflection on them that they failed to invent nuclear-powered submarines! We should judge the Greeks not by comparing their scientific conceptions with ours but by the contrasts between their points of view and those of earlier civilizations. On this basis our admiration for their achievements is bound to be great.

Greek science grew out of Greek speculative philosophy, a kind of thinking which they invented. Philosophy in its broadest sense is the search for a rational understanding of the universe in which we live. The nature and spirit of the inquiry can be judged from the remarks of Randall about the Greek philosopher Aristotle:

Aristotle's aim is to understand, to find out why things are as they are. It is not to control things, not to make them different from what they are.... For instance, physics for him is not "practical" but "theoretical": it is not expected to *do* anything, except to give understanding.... Aristotle aimed to understand Greece: he never forgot that aim. To understand the world of Greece meant for Aristotle three things: it meant an understanding of living, of knowing, and of talking.... To understand the world of Greece meant, first, an understanding of human life as something lived in human groups set in a physical environment.... Aristotle is convinced that no way of understanding the world, no scheme of "science," is worth its salt unless it provides the means for understanding living processes in general, and the processes of human living in particular.... Throughout Aristotle there runs this controlling biological and functional point of view.... In the second place, to understand the world of Greece meant for Aristotle an understanding of intelligence and reason ... as a natural and inevitable activity involved in human living, like breathing or digesting.... Intelligence, knowing, is the most important and most significant fact in the universe.... Thirdly, to understand the world of Greece means for Aristotle an understanding of

language, of discourse,... as the instrument of thinking and knowing....
The world is the kind of a world that can be talked about, in which things
can be distinguished and defined, in which we can reason from one statement
to another.... Knowledge and language are a flowering of the world, an
operation of its power to be understood and expressed.[8]

These remarks about the point of view of one of the central
figures in Greek philosophy indicate the acute and perceptive
thinking for which the Greeks are famous. The very idea of ration-
ality, which means so much in the modern world, seems almost to
have had its origin in Greece. We owe to the Greeks the development and systematic use of the basic distinction between appearance
and reality that was so woefully lacking in the thought of their
predecessors (cf. Sec. 1); so long as this distinction was not made,
there was no reason to ask questions of the kind that lead to
scientific discoveries. We owe them also the notion that the universe
is an orderly one that man can hope to understand. Their approach
to understanding was not experimental nor scientific in the modern
sense. It was made through a critical discussion of broad general
principles or insights, drawn from everyday experience.

Admittedly, the Greeks were only partially emancipated from
the primitive tendency to interpret natural phenomena in terms of
the actions of gods and spirits, but they did develop the conception
of impersonal law by which our experience and our observations
of the external world can be given an organized interpretation.
They had the idea of a mental model of the universe and the desire
to construct such a model. Their arguments led them to study the
art of reasoning, to debate the precise definitions of words, and so
to prepare the way for critical thinking in every domain of thought.

The greatest scientific success of the Greeks was in the field of
geometry. The Egyptians and Babylonians knew many specific
practical geometric facts, but it remained for the Greeks to unite
these and other such facts into a closely knit, logical structure. As
a starting point they chose a small set of *axioms* — broad, basic
assumptions that seemed too obvious to require justification.
From these axioms, or postulates, the fundamental laws of space
and space-relationships were deduced by rigorous logical argument.

In their development of geometry the Greeks were creating an
ideal for all future work in mathematics and the natural sciences.
To be sure, the basis of inquiry for the scientist of today is more
specialized. He starts from specific observations and experiments
in a limited field of inquiry, such as the motion of falling bodies.
On the basis of the available data he tries to frame simple mathematical laws that summarize the facts. By generalizing from the
first simple laws of observation, he tries to invent or discover laws
of broader scope that will organize a wider range of observational
facts. *The goal, however, is always the invention or discovery of a
small number of basic principles from which all the other relationships
in a broad area of investigation can be deduced.* The resulting final
theory can be cast in the form of a set of axioms and definitions
from which a logical network of theorems is deduced. Its formal,

---

[8] J. H. Randall, Jr., *Aristotle* (Columbia University Press, New York, 1960), Chap. 1.

logical structure then resembles that of Greek geometry. This structure and the influence of Greek mathematics are evident in Galileo's *Two New Sciences* and in the famous *Principia* in which Newton propounded his theories of motion and gravitation. In the scientific treatises of today the logical structure of theory is frequently covered over by lengthy discussions of the experimental background of the concepts, assumptions, and theorems involved, but, insofar as the work is sound and complete, it has a hidden resemblance to Greek geometry.

Unfortunately the Greek success in geometry and their partial success in astronomy were not, and could not be, followed by similar successes in the physical sciences. In comparison with physics and chemistry, geometry is a relatively simple subject for which suitable axioms could be selected intuitively without elaborate experimental investigations. The geometrical astronomy which they attempted is less simple, and physics and chemistry are not simple at all. The Greeks concentrated their attention on what seemed to them most important, the bias of their interest being toward politics, ethics, logic, and mathematics. They made careful astronomical observations, as had the Babylonians and Egyptians before them, but their science, especially in the period before the time of Alexander the Great, tended to be of the armchair variety, speculative rather than experimental.

We should not blame the Greeks for this speculative approach to science. They had no way of knowing in advance that a method brilliantly successful for geometry would prove a dismal failure for physics, and we must remember that they began the study of science with almost no measuring instruments. To be sure, they could measure distances and angles; with waterclocks and sundials they could measure time; weights they could determine with a balance. But that was about all. Moreover, the philosophers who dabbled in science lived in a society based on slavery. They themselves had little experience with any kind of manual work and little knowledge of the technical arts on which experimental measurements must be based. The remarkable thing about Greek science is not its weakness in physics and chemistry but its brilliant achievement in geometry and the good beginning it made in astronomy.

3.2. Greek science was by no means "all of a piece." The history of Greek ideas is one of conflicting currents and crosscurrents to which we cannot do justice here. In its earliest period we find the Ionian philosophers Thales (*c.* 640–546 B.C.), Anaximander, Anaximenes, and Heraclitus opposing the stories of creation in the mythology of the Babylonians and Egyptians by attempting to formulate an impersonal naturalistic theory. Thales, for example, suggested that the known universe had in some way evolved out of a single substance, water. This speculation was an attempt to reconcile the ever-recurrent transformation of matter by heat, cold, and biological processes with the permanent and unchanging character of the broader features of the physical universe. His conception was an impersonal one that ignored the creator-gods of the Babylonians and the Egyptians.

The ideas of Thales and the other Ionians were crude. Their specific hypotheses were all wrong, but their efforts to understand the natural world, when properly examined in relation to their own times, show reflection and discernment of a high order. Leucippus (flourished *c.* 475 B.C.) and Democritus (*c.* 470–*c.* 400 B.C.), originators of the first atomic theory, approached their doctrine from the same intellectual perspective. These men had a highly rational approach to the vast questions which they posed.[9] However, their attempts to deal with such difficult topics as the nature of matter and the evolutionary process were premature. They did not realize that trustworthy answers to the questions they asked can be reached only by a succession of generalizations based on a painstaking study of the simplest natural processes.

3.3. A quite different stream of scientific thought was initiated by Pythagoras, from whom we inherit the theorem that the square of the hypotenuse of a right-angled triangle is equal to the sum of the squares of its other sides. Pythagoras was a mathematician, experimentalist, philosopher, and mystic, born at Samos, near the coast of Asia Minor, *c.* 582 B.C. When Persian attacks threatened the eastern shore of the Aegean, he emigrated to the Greek colony at Crotona, near the southern end of the Italian peninsula. There he founded a secret religious brotherhood devoted to "the practice of asceticism and the study of mathematics."

Pythagoras was destined to exert an enormous influence (but a mixed one) on the development of scientific thought through the centuries to come. On the one hand, he and his followers made valuable contributions to the development of mathematics and science; on the other hand, an element of mystical madness went into their studies that continued to fascinate and mislead their successors down to the time of Newton. Basic to the philosophy of the Pythagoreans was the notion that numbers have a real significance outside the minds of men. In fact, the Pythagoreans regarded numbers as the key to the riddle of the universe. Individual numbers were thought to have an occult meaning that seems very strange to scientists and mathematicians today, but it survives in the popular superstition regarding the number 13.

The great Socrates (469–399 B.C.) was neither a scientist nor a mathematician but a penetrating moral and social philosopher who directed the attention of men away from the physical world toward the problem of good and evil. He brought to bear on the customs and standards of his time a relentlessly critical mind, and by his insistence on the exact use of language undoubtedly helped to prepare the way for the science that was to come.

In an introduction to science we can hardly hope to do justice to such a man as Plato (427–347 B.C.), but no attempt to sketch the beginnings of science can very well leave him out. His attitude toward nature and his ideas about nature were highly unscientific, but his thinking commands our admiration. His influence on the intellectual history of our western culture was enormous.

---

[9] Benjamin Farrington, in Vol. 1 of *Greek Science* (Penguin Books, Ltd., Harmondsworth, England, 1944), gives an excellent account of the development of Greek scientific ideas down to the time of Aristotle.

Plato was a bold, creative thinker and at the same time a poet and dramatist, a prophet, aristocrat, and mystic. He was deeply influenced by the Pythagoreans as well as by his own immediate predecessor and teacher, Socrates. From the latter he absorbed a low opinion of the possibilities of physical science, and the conviction that the more important kind of knowledge open to the human mind is knowledge of the meaning and aim of human life, the highest good of the soul. Such knowledge, moreover, unlike that offered by incipient physical science, seemed necessary and certain. Socrates taught by interrogation and conversation; Plato's writings are in dialogue form. From Pythagoras came a high respect for mathematics, especially geometry, and a willingness to read into mathematical relations a mystical meaning we no longer recognize. Plato introduced the important mathematical concept of negative numbers. He was interested in logic; in fact it is believed that the precise and logical form of Euclid's geometry with its exactly stated assumptions, theorems, and corollaries, is due largely to Plato's influence. He sharply opposed the nonreligious mechanical philosophy of the early Ionian thinkers.

Plato insisted that the good and the just are not the inventions or conventions of human societies but discoveries rooted in the rational structure of the cosmos. Whereas Socrates emphasized the importance of general and abstract ideas, for Plato such ideas, which are essential to mathematics and other kinds of abstract thought, came to possess a reality denied to the individual concrete objects and events that make up the chaotic changing world of experience. Ocean waves, which merely come and go, are but appearances; the *idea* of a wave is timeless. Individual cats are born and die, but the *idea* of a cat is timeless. And surely what is permanent is more real than what is evanescent! So the world of the logical mind was conceived by Plato to be the supreme reality of which the objects and occurrences of daily life are but imperfect shadows.

Plato believed with the Pythagoreans and with Socrates that moral purpose rules the universe. In his view the laws of the physical universe, like the laws of the spiritual universe, are expressions of a cosmic drive toward perfection. The earth and the sky are spherical *because* the sphere is the perfect figure. The stars are in circular motion *because* this simplest of all motions is the perfect motion. On earth we have change, decay, and all sorts of ugliness, but the heavens are the seat of sublime beauty and changeless perfection.

To Plato the somewhat irregular apparent motions of the wandering planets in the sky were an offense that must be explained away. Pythagoras had discovered that the observed motion of the sun relative to the earth could be regarded as a combination of a uniform circular motion of the celestial sphere and a much slower uniform circular motion of the sun along the ecliptic.[10] Plato accordingly proposed that the astronomers undertake the task of

---

[10] In Chap. 2, Sec. 7.8, we noted that the line of sight between the earth and the sun does not have an exactly uniform angular velocity on the ecliptic. In the time of Pythagoras, however, the nonuniformity of the sun's motion on the ecliptic had not yet been discovered.

resolving the motion of the planets into a superposition of uniform circular motions — a proposal that was to influence astronomical theory in a decisive way for 2000 years. (His basic conception is akin to mathematical methods used today in the study of wave motion.)

From the standpoint of modern science this emphasis on purpose and perfection in nature was unfortunate. Believing, in an age in which the mechanical order of the world of physics and chemistry had not yet been discovered, that the order of the universe as a whole is basically a moral one, it was natural for Plato to seek indications of moral order in all natural phenomena. Religious people today believe with Plato in the overarching moral order of the universe and regard it as a reflection of divine purpose. On the other hand, the prime achievement of modern science is the discovery that the events and processes we observe in the physical world are controlled in detail by a system of universal "mechanical," or mathematical, laws that can be formulated without reference to purpose.[11]

The whole problem of the relation of the physical universe to our instinctive sense of purpose is difficult and confusing. We all tend to interpret the phenomena of anatomy and physiology in terms of purpose. The heart pumps blood through the arteries and veins. The blood carries nourishment to our tissues and takes away waste products. Our instinct is to say that the heart, the blood vessels, and the blood must have been made *in order* to carry nourishment throughout the body. But shall we say that rivers were made *in order* to carry rain water back to the sea? Does the sun rise in the morning *in order* to give us heat and light? Experience shows that the answers we give to these questions are irrelevant to investigation of the detailed laws governing such natural processes. In fact, the interpretation of such processes in terms of purpose tends to shut off questions of detail that are the starting points of fruitful scientific investigation. This is true in large measure even in biology, where organization and function play a very important role.

The question of the ultimate meaning of the universe remains a philosophical one to which science as such can give no final answer. It is still the riddle of the ages — perhaps the most important question with which human beings are confronted.

3.4. Aristotle (384–323 B.C.), pupil of Plato and tutor of Alexander the Great, lived during the political decline and fall of Athens. He witnessed Alexander's conquests and died a year after the young emperor.

The nature of Aristotle's philosophic and scientific inquiry is indicated in the quotations from Randall in Sec. 3.1 of this chapter. His voluminous written works range over physical and biological science, logic and metaphysics, ethics, politics, and poetry. He began

---

[11] There is no logical proof that exceptions to the rules, or to the uniformity of nature, cannot and do not occur. But everyday experience informs us that stones released in mid-air that do not fall are so rare that it makes sense to disregard them. Just so, the evidence of centuries of scientific testing is overwhelmingly in favor of the belief that Nature has a fixed book of impersonal rules, which she makes a habit of following.

where Plato left off, and there is much of Plato in his thought. But he was an observer as well as a thinker. In the end he reacted against the efforts of Socrates and Plato to formulate a philosophy of nature based solely on broad general arguments unconnected with the systematic gathering and organization of scientific facts. With Aristotle began the collection and organization of such facts. This was the first step toward the development of the specialization which characterized the new scientific era that followed the breakup of Alexander's empire.

Although Aristotle's biological writings were of high quality and show that he was a keen observer, his attempts at dealing with physics and chemistry (of which we shall hear more in Chaps. 4 and 6) were less happy. Whereas we base biology on physics and chemistry, Aristotle turned the relation around and tried to base physical science on biology. He tried to understand the motions of falling bodies and biological transformations as different examples of the same kind of process in a world in which the moral order is supreme. Confusing misconceptions, some of them inherited from the Pythagorean-Platonic school, were given the weight of Aristotle's authority. In the course of the centuries his writings were to be transmitted through the Arabian culture to the re-awakening intellectual world of Europe at the time of the Revival of Learning. In his own day Aristotle, man of genius, was a great logician, philosopher, and scientific pathbreaker; but by a paradox of history his name was eventually to become the symbol of blind and sterile authority.

Shortly after the death of Alexander, the intellectual center of the Greek world shifted to the new city of Alexandria, in Egypt, where a Greek dynasty was set up by Ptolemy I, one of Alexander's friends and generals. There Ptolemy created a university and a library that at one time contained 400,000 volumes of manuscript books. The library remained intact until A.D. 390 and was not totally destroyed until A.D. 640. The university, or "Museum," was the center for a brilliant development of the special sciences that began to decline in vigor after about 100 years but remained alive into the second century A.D. Here, in an atmosphere more practical and less metaphysical than that of Athens, medicine, astronomy, geography, mechanics, and mathematics were cultivated with remarkable success. The pursuit of philosophic generality was largely abandoned in favor of the study of definite and limited problems.[12] The emphasis placed by Aristotle on dissection and careful observation in his biological studies was continued. Observational astronomy came into its own.

Among the famous names of Alexandrian science were those of Euclid, Apollonius, Eratosthenes, and the three great astronomers, Aristarchus, Hipparchus, and Claudius Ptolemy. Archimedes of Syracuse, perhaps the greatest scientist of the ancient world, was reckoned a member of the "Alexandrian school," though his connection was that of a student and correspondent rather than resident.

---

[12] William Cecil Dampier, *A History of Science* (Cambridge University Press, Cambridge, 1949), p. xiv.

4. Early Greek Astronomical Theories

4.1. Among the physical sciences, astronomy, with its close relation to geometry, was cultivated most assiduously and with the most valuable results.[13] The simple majesty of the night sky fills every beholder with awe. It was inevitable that it should be an object of major interest to the ancient Greek philosophers as they strove to understand the world about them. Their observations and speculations prepared the way for Copernicus and the wonders of the astronomy of today.

Recognition of the spherical form of the earth goes back to the early Pythagoreans. Philolaus (*c.* 450 B.C.), a Pythagorean contemporary of Socrates, saw that the apparent rotation of the stars from east to west could be explained most simply by assuming that the earth itself is in rotation from west to east. Convinced, however, that ten is the perfect number, he proposed an astronomical scheme based on the assumption of ten heavenly bodies. Five planets were known at that time. To them Philolaus added five other bodies, the sun, the moon, the earth, the sphere of the stars, and a hypothetical body called the counter-earth. The earth and the counter-earth were assumed to rotate together around a fixed "central fire," always hidden from us because it is under foot. The counter-earth served to shield the back side of the earth from the heat and light given off by the central fire. Two other early Pythagoreans, Hicetas and Ecphantus, are believed to have modified the doctrine of Philolaus by asserting that the earth rotates about an axis through its own center rather than around a central fire.

4.2. We have referred in Sec. 3.3 to Plato's suggestion that planetary motion should be resolved into a combination of uniform circular motions. This idea was followed up by Plato's pupil, the mathematician and astronomer Eudoxus (403–356 B.C.), whose observatory at Cnidus, according to some accounts, was standing as late as the beginning of the Christian era. Eudoxus worked out an ingenious and fairly successful scheme for describing planetary motions by means of a succession of invisible spheres concentric with the earth.[14] He supposed that each planet is carried on the equator of a sphere that rotates uniformly about an axis fixed in a second sphere just outside the first. The second sphere in turn rotates uniformly about a different axis fixed in the next sphere, and so on. Four or five spheres were required for each planet, the outermost being in every case the sphere of the stars.

Although the theory of concentric spheres was shortly to be abandoned by the professional astronomers of the Alexandrian school, it was in favor long enough to receive the approval of Aristotle — a junior contemporary of Eudoxus. Through the writings of Aristotle the notion that the planets, like the stars, are attached to invisible "crystalline" spheres rotating about the

---

[13] In this brief account of the highlights of a confusing and controversial story, the author has placed his chief reliance on the authority of J. L. E. Dreyer, *A History of Astronomy from Thales to Kepler* (Dover Publishing Co., New York, 1953).

[14] T. S. Kuhn, *The Copernican Revolution* (Harvard University Press, Cambridge, Mass., 1957), pp. 55–59; J. L. E. Dreyer, *op. cit.*, Chap. 4.

earth in a combination of uniform circular motions was transmitted to western Europe at the time of the Revival of Learning. The medieval cosmology described by Dante was based upon it.

Arguing against the scheme of Philolaus, Aristotle asserts in his treatise *On the Heavens* that the earth must be at rest, since there is obviously no force to cause it to move. To modern ears he is more convincing when he points out that the spherical shape of the earth is proved by the form of its shadow on the moon during a lunar eclipse and by the changes in the position of stars relative to the horizon as one journeys north or south (see Chap. 2, Sec. 1).

5.1. Another major figure in the development of Greek astronomical theory was Heracleides of Pontus, a contemporary of Aristotle. Following the proposal of Hicetas and Ecphantus, Heracleides taught that the apparent westward rotation of the celestial sphere is due to an eastward rotation of the earth about an axis through its own center directed toward the north celestial pole. He went on to suggest that the inferior planets, Venus and Mercury, revolve about the sun, and thus he prepared the way for the development of a complete heliocentric conception of the motions of the earth and the other planets by Aristarchus in the next generation.

Heracleides and Aristarchus were far in advance of their time; their ideas did not win general credence among the philosophers of their day. In fact these ideas were generally ignored for nearly two thousand years. But in the end it was from the suggestions of Heracleides and Aristarchus that the monk Copernicus, in the sixteenth century A.D., developed his conception of the astronomical universe and so touched off the revolution that led to modern science. The writings of the two early forerunners of Copernicus are lost, except for the treatise *On the Distances of the Sun and Moon*, in which Aristarchus reports the measurements described in Chap. 2, Sec. 8. Hence, we cannot be sure of their arguments. Nevertheless, it is worth while to consider the astronomical evidence available to them and the probable line of reasoning that led them to the heliocentric conception.[15]

5.2. Consider first the daily rotation of the celestial sphere relative to the earth. We do not observe that the earth is stationary. Nor can we observe that the celestial sphere is stationary. What we do observe is a relative motion. In everyday life it is convenient to think of the earth as at rest — to make the earth's surface a frame of reference which defines what we mean by "at rest" and "in motion." It was quite natural that the ancients should have used the same frame of reference in the study of astronomy. But so far as the geometrical facts are concerned we can with

5. The Sun as a Center of Rotation

[15] The evidence available to the Greeks is still available today. We have much more evidence than they had, but what they knew, if carefully considered, was sufficient to provide a good argument in favor of a sun-centered planetary system including the earth. To develop such an argument is to deepen one's understanding of the astronomy of today.

equal right assume that the celestial sphere rotates from east to west about a stationary earth *or* that the earth rotates from west to east inside a stationary celestial sphere. In the latter case we make the celestial sphere an astronomical frame of reference that can be used to define corresponding coordinates, such as declination and right ascension.

If we had only the earth and the stars to consider, there would be little but prejudice to make either choice preferable. But the motions of the sun, moon, and planets relative to the celestial sphere are much simpler than their motions relative to the earth. If we assume, with Heracleides, that the earth rotates inside a fixed concentric celestial sphere, the motions of the sun, moon, and planets in right ascension and declination are their true angular motions. We already have seen, for example (cf. Chap. 1, Sec. 6), that the angular motion of the sun relative to the celestial sphere is a regular annual progression about the great circle of the ecliptic — a much simpler motion than its north-and-south spiral-ing motion with respect to the earth's surface. Thus the hypoth-esis of Heracleides gives a simplified conception of the true motion of the sun, as indeed it does for the motions of the moon and the planets. In all these cases the observed motions relative to the earth are combinations of the rapid daily rotation of the celestial sphere relative to the earth and its comparatively slow and simple motions over the celestial sphere. In fact, whether astro-nomers accepted the hypothesis of Heracleides or not, they were bound to make use of the simplified descriptions of the motions of the heavenly bodies that result from the adoption of the celestial sphere as a frame of reference. From this point of view, the con-ception of a rotating earth was at the least very plausible.

The acceptance of the idea that the stars are stationary while the earth rotates "underneath them" has one important conse-quence unknown to either Heracleides or Aristarchus: It requires a reinterpretation of the phenomenon of the precession of the equinoxes (cf. Chap. 1, Sec. 9). In our original fixed-earth inter-pretation the "axis of the sky" was thought of as the axis of rotation of the celestial sphere. But from our present point of view it is the axis of the earth's own spinning motion. Hence the slow 26,000-year cycle of the motion of the celestial poles relative to the stars must now be thought of as a consequence of a slow "precessional" motion of the earth's axis of spin in space. It is not the sky, but the earth, that moves with the gyroscopic pre-cession of a spinning top. On this basis, many centuries later, it was possible for Isaac Newton to work out a quantitative mechanical explanation for the phenomenon of precession.

5.3. Let us consider next the teaching of Heracleides with respect to the inferior planets, Venus and Mercury [see item (*b*), Sec. 9 of Chap. 2]. As previously mentioned the paths of all planets relative to the celestial sphere are in the belt of the zodiac close to the ecliptic. Like the sun, they move generally eastward among the stars. Moreover, the inferior planets are distinguished from the others because the average time they require to pass around the zodiacal belt is exactly the same as for the sun. Each inferior planet oscillates back and forth relative to the sun, alternately preceding it and following it. The oscillations of Venus relative to the sun carry it from a maximum backward elongation of about 47° to a maximum forward elongation of essentially the same magnitude and back again, the whole cycle taking a period of 584 days. Mercury's maximum elongation is 28°, and its period of oscillation (synodic period) is 116 days. Because these planets are never far removed from the sun, they are to be seen either as "evening stars" that follow the sun over the western horizon at nightfall, or as "morning stars" that rise over the eastern horizon shortly before the sun.

The oscillatory motion of each of the inferior planets relative to the sun is what we would expect to observe if the planet were in rotation about the sun in an orbit whose plane coincides approximately with the plane of the ecliptic. Hence, it was natural for Heracleides, sharing in the Greek preference for uniform circular motions, to interpret the behavior of the planets Venus and Mercury in terms of such uniform circular orbital motions about the sun. This was and is the simplest possible interpretation of the known facts; Figure 3–1 illustrates the conception in a diagram in which the celestial sphere is the fixed frame of reference.

This second new hypothesis has marked advantages. In the first place, it explains why the inferior planets should have retrograde motions at and near alternate conjunctions with the sun. The true velocity v_t in space of an inferior planet, say Venus, should be a compound of the sun's velocity v_s and the velocity of Venus relative to the sun,[16] say v_r. If we assume that the direction of rotation of Venus in its motion about the sun is the same as that of the sun about the earth, the velocity of Venus relative to the sun v_r at superior conjunction (the point a in Fig. 3–1) is in the same direction as the velocity of the sun v_s. Hence, the absolute velocity of Venus v_t is equal to $v_s + v_r$. At this point, then, Venus is moving eastward like the sun, but more rapidly. On the other hand, at the point of inferior conjunction c the relative velocity v_r is opposite in direction to v_s. If v_r is greater than v_s, as we may suppose, the combined true velocity v_t will also be opposite in direction to the sun's velocity. Hence, the planet will be seen momentarily to move *westward* along the zodiac. Figure 3–2 spells out the story by showing a succession of positions of the sun with the corresponding positions of Venus, tracing the path of Venus in space. Position V_1 corresponds to a in Fig. 3–1 while V_6 is in a region of retrograde motion near inferior conjunction.

The explanation is an unforced deduction from the basic assumption, provided only that we make the assumption definite by attributing a suitable relative velocity to Venus. It holds for Mercury as well as for Venus.

Moreover, the hypothesis explains why retrograde motion should occur at every other conjunction. It explains why it takes much longer for the inferior planets to pass from the position of maximum lagging elongation (d) to the position of maximum

[16] Velocities are compounded like forces by the parallelogram or triangle method, as we shall see in Chap. 7, Sec. 4.

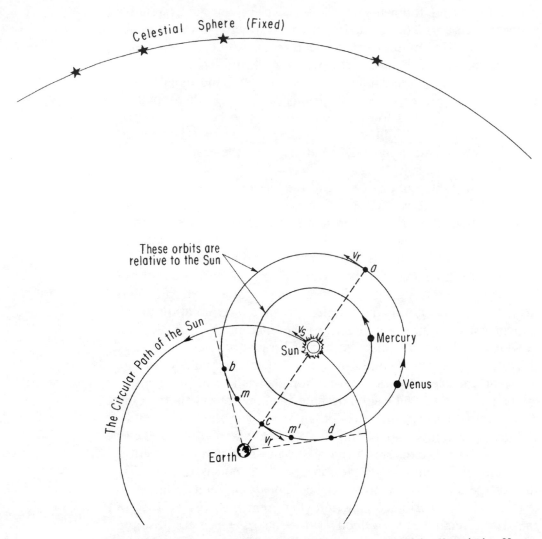

Fig. 3–1. *The Motion of the Inferior Planets, as Conceived by Heracleides.* Heracleides supposed that the sun travels around the earth in a circular path and that simultaneously the inferior planets Venus and Mercury travel around the sun in circular orbits in approximately the same plane as the sun's orbit, i.e., the plane of the ecliptic. In the diagram all the orbital motions are taken to be counterclockwise.

At point *a* Venus is passing the sun on its far side. We call this a point of *superior conjunction.* At *c* Venus passes between us and the sun. This is called a point of *inferior conjunction.* At *b* the angle of elongation between Venus and the sun has its maximum value in the forward direction. At this point Venus, which has been gaining on the sun as they move together around the earth, turns and begins to fall back relative to the sun.

forward elongation (*b*) than to drop back to the position of maximum lag again. It explains why, on the average, each of these inferior planets keeps pace with the sun.

Finally, and most important, the assumption that Venus and Mercury rotate in circular orbits about the sun does much to explain the periodic variations in the brightness of the various planets. These variations in brightness are very striking in the case of Venus and Mars. In all instances they are correlated, like the retrograde motions, with the synodic period — the time between successive conjunctions of the same kind (cf. Chap. 2, Sec. 9). These pulsations in brightness seemed to the ancients to imply cyclic changes in the distance from the earth to each of the planets in question. In fact, we are informed[17] that it was the impossibility of reconciling the theory of Eudoxus with variations in the distances of the planets which led to the abandonment of that theory.

The observed brightness of Venus is at a minimum at the superior conjunction where, according to Heracleides, the planet is farthest from the earth. As the theoretical distance decreases, the brightness increases to a maximum at a point near m on Fig. 3–1. Thence it decreases toward zero as the planet approaches inferior conjunction at c. Beyond that point the brightness increases to a second maximum at m', then gradually fades again as the planet recedes from the earth. Clearly, changes in distance *can* account for the major fact that the two points of maximum brightness occur when Venus is close to its minimum distance from the earth. They *can not* explain why the brightness fades again near the inferior conjunction.[18] But that could be regarded as a secondary phenomenon. Unfortunately, we do not know the extent of Heracleides' knowledge of the brightness phenomenon, nor what he thought of it.

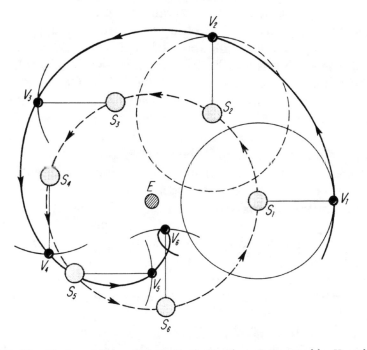

Fig. 3–2. *The Motion of Venus Relative to the Earth, as Interpreted by Heracleides.* Here $S_1, S_2, \cdots, S_6$ are a succession of positions of the sun as it moves in a circle about the earth E. Venus rotates about the sun as a center and takes the successive positions $V_1, V_2, \cdots, V_6$. As seen from the earth, its normal motion relative to the distant background of stars is reversed at V_6.

5.4. And so we come to Aristarchus of Samos, frequently described as the "Copernicus of antiquity." He was a pupil of Strato, one of the leaders in the establishment of the Museum school at Alexandria.

[17] J. L. E. Dreyer, *op. cit.*, p. 141.

[18] We know today that this is because Venus shines by reflected light. The planet goes through a cycle of phases like those of the moon. At inferior conjunction the dark side of the sphere is directed toward the earth.

Aristarchus accepted the assumptions of Heracleides regarding the axial rotation of the earth and the motion of the planets Venus and Mercury relative to the sun. He apparently went on to postulate that the superior planets and the earth itself revolve about the sun. In other words, he seems to have formulated the complete heliocentric conception on which modern astronomy is based. It would appear from the comments of later authors that he did not work out many details.

The assumption that the earth is not the center of creation but is a planet, like Venus and Mercury, with an orbital motion about the sun in addition to its daily rotation on its own axis, was in those days a very bold hypothesis. How did Aristarchus come to make it? Here the speculations of the nineteenth-century astronomer Schiaparelli[19] provide a probable answer.

5.5. The superior planet Mars, like Venus, goes through striking changes in brightness during its synodic period. It is brightest when in opposition to the sun and overhead at midnight. It is least bright as it approaches conjunction with the sun. If it has a circular orbit, as any Greek philosopher would assume, that orbit must enclose the earth but cannot have its center at the earth. The orbit must be eccentric to the earth, and the center must so be placed that Mars approaches close to the earth when opposite the sun but is very far from the earth when in conjunction with the sun. In short, the center of the orbit of Mars must be displaced from the earth toward the sun, somewhere on the line joining the earth and the sun. As this line rotates with the sun, the center of the orbit of Mars must itself rotate about the earth as a second center. The center *could* be anywhere on the earth–sun line far enough away to fit in with the great changes in brightness of Mars, but the simplest and most appealing possibility was to locate the center at the sun, as shown in Fig. 3–3. In that case the only difference between the orbit of Mars and those of the inferior planets Venus and Mercury is that the former is large enough to enclose the earth, whereas the latter are not. In all three cases the orbits are centered at the sun.

The same argument applies to the planets Jupiter and Saturn, though the variations in brightness of these planets are less conspicuous than those of Mars. If we assign sun-centered orbits to these planets also, the radii of those orbits must be greater than that of Mars if the ratio of the smallest and largest distance from the earth is to fit the lesser changes in brightness.

The resulting picture of the planetary motions is one in which all five planets revolve about the sun in orbits that increase in radius progressively from Mercury through Venus, Mars, Jupiter, to Saturn. The sun itself revolves about the earth as before. *This is, in fact, the planetary theory adopted in the sixteenth century by the Danish astronomer Tycho Brahe and known today as the Tychonic system.* It provides an unforced explanation of the retrograde motions of the superior planets on the assumption that the velocities of these planets relative to the sun v_r are *less* than the

[19] The argument is discussed by J. L. E. Dreyer, *op. cit.*, pp. 141–147.

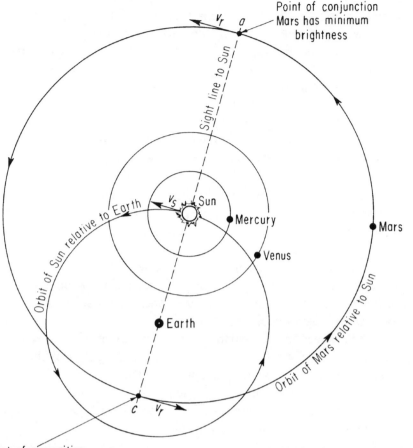

Fig. 3–3. *The Tychonic System for Mercury, Venus, and Mars.* In this figure the sun is conceived to move in a circular orbit about the fixed earth, while Mars as well as Mercury and Venus revolve in circular orbits about the moving sun. The point *a* of the relative orbit of Mars is the point of conjunction with the sun as seen from the earth. At this point Mars is farthest from the earth and least bright. At point *c* Mars is in opposition to the sun. Its distance from the earth is a minimum and its brightness a maximum. This is also the point of maximum retrograde motion.

velocity of the sun v_s. At the moment of opposition (point c in Fig. 3–3) the velocity v_s is opposite in direction to v_r and makes a westward contribution to the planet's apparent motion along the zodiac. If v_r is less than v_s, the latter velocity will dominate and the planet will go through a phase of retrograde motion.

5.6. We do not know for certain whether Aristarchus invented this Tychonic system as one step in the development of his theory or not, but, as Dreyer remarks, it is difficult to see how else he could have reached his final conclusion. The system is simple and in first approximation remarkably effective in representing the geometrical facts. But if Aristarchus did invent it, he did not stop at this point. In the earth-centered Tychonic system it is *assumed* that the earth is stationary except for its axial rotation. The annual motion of the sun about the earth is then inferred from the fact that the sun, as seen from the earth, is projected against a moving point on the celestial sphere. But the same annual motion of the line of sight from the earth to the sun along the ecliptic would also be produced if the earth had an annual orbital motion around a stationary sun. If we make the assumption that the sun is stationary and the earth in motion, we merely look at the earth and the planets from the point of view of an observer on the sun. This seems legitimate. On this view if Mercury, Venus, Mars, Jupiter, and Saturn are in rotation about the sun as previously supposed, the earth rotates with them in the same direction. The conception of the solar system so arrived at is the heliocentric conception proposed by Aristarchus and adopted much later by Copernicus.

On this basis it is easy to establish the following points:

(a) In the new frame of reference the earth rotates about the stationary sun in an orbit whose radius is the same as that of the sun in the earth-centered Tychonic frame. The plane of the orbit is the plane of the ecliptic.

(b) The motion of each planet relative to the sun is the same as before, but in the new scheme this simple rotation is the only planetary motion. (The complete system of orbits, still nearly coplanar, is mapped on Fig. 4–1.)

(c) The speed of the earth in the new scheme, being equal to the speed of the sun in the old, is intermediate between the speeds of the inferior planets and the speeds of the superior planets.

(d) The earth and the five planets taken together form a harmonious succession of bodies whose speeds decrease in a regular progression as their orbital radii increase.

Clearly, then, the new scheme is qualitatively satisfactory and much simpler than the Tychonic scheme. As a representation of the relative motions of the sun and planets it is just as good as the Tychonic system and no better. If the motions of the planets are taken to be uniform circular motions with the sun as a common center, the scheme is *not* quantitatively accurate. However, as we shall see in Chap. 4, it is possible to fit the observed astronomical data accurately on the basis of this model of the solar system, provided we admit orbits that depart somewhat from the uniform circular pattern.

In making his imaginative leap from a fixed-earth system to a fixed-sun system. Aristarchus may have been guided in part by the indication (Chap. 2, Sec. 8) that the earth is intermediate in size between the moon and the sun. He knew that the moon, which is smaller than the earth, revolves about the earth. Would it not be more sensible to suppose that the earth, which seems to be smaller than the sun, revolves about the sun than to suppose that the larger sun revolves about the smaller earth? At any rate, we learn from Archimedes that Aristarchus supposed "that the fixed stars and the sun are immovable, but that the earth is carried around the sun in a circle which is in the middle of the course."

5.7. Unfortunately this new conception did not appeal to many of Aristarchus' contemporaries. There were prejudices and arguments on the other side. Presumably, the heliocentric model was not presented as a result of adopting a new and convenient frame of reference, but as a matter of objective fact. On that basis the proposal was completely out of step with the physics and the philosophy of the time. The ancient belief that the earth is at the stationary center of a spherical universe was deeply rooted in the philosophy of common sense. Despite the Pythagoreans, most Greek thinkers were not ready to abandon it.

The belief was not an isolated one that could be set aside without destroying the fabric of philosophic thought. To the ancients the contrast between the terrestrial world about them and the celestial domain of sun, moon, and stars was overwhelming. On earth are summer and winter, growth and decay, endless disorder and triviality. On high is a vast domain of changeless rhythmic motion, the seat of divine powers that regulate the seasons and so the life of man and beast. This sharp distinction between the terrestrial and celestial regions was basic to nearly all Greek philosophic thinking. It was inconsistent with the notion that the earth is a satellite of the sun.

Aristotle's ideas about force and motion on earth were inapplicable to the motion of celestial bodies. For him an explanation of the motion of planets and stars could be furnished "only by either supposing an external agent, a prime mover, an astral intelligence, or endowing the stars with a life of their own."[20] Because it was only recently that they had stopped thinking of celestial motions in terms of animistic ideas, the Greeks of the third century B.C. were not ready for a unified mechanical theory of terrestrial physics and celestial motions. So they were unprepared to appreciate the advantages of the heliocentric conception which many centuries later was to pave the way for the Newtonian mechanical explanation of the solar system.

There were, moreover, specific physical objections to the proposal. If the earth were in motion, why should not light objects, such as autumn leaves, blow off its surface? Why does a stone thrown vertically into the air return to its starting point? If the earth swings in a giant orbit about the sun, how can it remain at the center of the celestial sphere throughout the year? Surely, if such a motion did exist, we would observe a variation in the angular separation of pairs of stars in the orbital plane as the earth approaches them and then recedes from them.

To this last criticism Aristarchus replied that the variations in angular separation of the stars would be too small to detect if the celestial sphere were large enough in comparison with the earth's orbit. We know today that the distances of the vast majority of stars that define the celestial sphere are millions of times the distance of the sun from the earth, but to the contemporaries of Aristarchus a celestial sphere on that scale was undreamed of.

Did Aristarchus make any attempt to fit his theory to the available records of planetary positions by introducing suitable orbital radii and orbital periods? A faithful representation of the data in this way would have solved the problem of astronomical prediction — a problem of great practical importance as long as men believed in astrology — and would almost inevitably have won the support of the astronomers. There is no record of any such quantitative application of the theory, but it is hard to believe that

---

[20] Max Jammer, *Concepts of Force* (Harvard University Press, Cambridge, Mass., 1957), p. 40.

Aristarchus did not make the attempt. His measurement of the relative distances of the sun and moon shows that he realized the importance of numerical magnitudes. We know that Calippus, in the generation before Aristarchus, worked hard to fit the concentric spheres of Eudoxus to the detailed numerical data, and that from the time of Aristarchus onward the accumulation of exact observations and the formulation of an exact mathematical representation of the data came to be the focal interests of the Alexandrian astronomers.

It seems probable, therefore, that Aristarchus did try to fit his theory to the records. In that case, he must have been disappointed with the results. The motions of the planets relative to the sun and the stars are *not* uniform circular motions about the sun as a center. The beautiful heliocentric model of the solar system, despite its qualitative success, cannot be made to reproduce the observations of planetary positions with accuracy unless that fact is taken into account. And so the argument that should have clinched the case for the heliocentric universe was not forthcoming.

6. The Epicycle-Deferent Stage in Greek Astronomy

After Aristarchus the great names of Alexandrian astronomy were Apollonius of Perga[21] (*fl.* 220 B.C.), Hipparchus[22] (*c.* 190–120 B.C.), and Claudius Ptolemy of Alexandria (*fl.* A.D. 170). These men avoided speculative theory and returned to the philosophically acceptable geocentric frame of reference. To account for the motions of the sun, moon and planets relative to the celestial sphere, they introduced a system of compounded circular motions similar in many ways to that of Heracleides, but much more complicated.

They employed three different devices to represent the observed motions with respect to the earth: the *epicycle*, the *eccentric circle*, and the *equant*. The best known of these is the *epicycle* shown in Fig. 3–4a. In the simple case shown, a planet at P moves on a small circle, called an epicycle, whose center C travels in the same direction about a larger circle called the *deferent*. The center of the deferent circle was identified originally with the position of the earth, but the center of the epicycle was *not* in general assumed to coincide with the position of any third body. To represent the behavior of one of the inferior planets, the center of the epicycle must keep pace with the sun as the center moves along the deferent circle, the period of the planet on the epicycle being shorter than the period (one solar year) on the deferent. To represent the motion of one of the superior planets, however, the period on the epicycle is one solar year, whereas the period on the deferent is longer than a year. Since the epicycle–deferent device differs from that of Heracleides for the inferior planets only in failing to put the

[21] Apollonius is chiefly famous for his work on the geometry of the plane curves known to us as conic sections — the circle, the ellipse, the hyperbola, and the parabola.

[22] The great astronomer Hipparchus was mentioned in Chap. 1, Sec. 9 as the discoverer of the precession of the equinoxes. He also discovered the nonuniformity of the sun's motion along the ecliptic. He developed the mathematics of plane and spherical trigonometry — tools absolutely essential to the modern astronomer — and invented a number of instruments to facilitate astronomical observations. His observatory was at Rhodes.

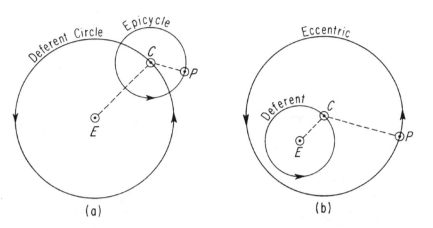

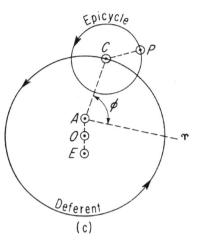

Fig. 3–4. *Mathematical Devices to Represent Planetary Motions.* Diagram *a*: the epicycle. Diagram *b*: the moving eccentric. Diagram *c*: the equant.

sun at the epicycle center *C*, it should be clear that the scheme can give a qualitative account of the several retrograde motions.

The device of the moving *eccentric circle* shown in Fig. 3–4*b* is a special case of the epicycle in which the planet travels on the larger circle, whose center moves on the smaller. This scheme with suitable dimensions and periods is mathematically equivalent to the normal epicycle arrangement of Diagram *a*.

The third device was a modification of the epicycle-deferent scheme in which the center of the deferent is located at a fixed point *O* at some distance from the earth (Fig. 3–4*c*). Moreover, the angular speed of the center of the epicycle is not constant relative to the earth *E* or to the center of the deferent *O* but is constant when measured with respect to a point *A* on the opposite side of *O* from *E* and at the same distance from *O* as *E*. The point *A* was called the equalizing point or equant point; the scheme as a whole is referred to as the *equant* scheme. As we know today, the true trajectories of the planets about the sun are eccentric ellipses traversed at speeds that increase and decrease as the planets approach the sun and recede from it. The equant was a remarkable invention that allowed the astronomer to describe important features of this motion in terms of circles and uniformly increasing angles.

Although the first two devices were known to Apollonius and Hipparchus, these astronomers did not work out a complete systematic representation of the observed motions of the various heavenly bodies. This accomplishment was left to Ptolemy, three centuries after Hipparchus. Ptolemy discarded the moving eccentric circles, introduced equants, and superposed epicycles on epicycles in order to describe the observed motions more faithfully. The final theoretical synthesis was anything but simple. Nevertheless, as a mathematical representation of an exceedingly complex array of geometrical facts it was a major achievement. It did fit the data available in the second century A.D. quite well. The theory was described in detail in a treatise on astronomy written by Ptolemy and known for many centuries as the *Almagest*. This comprehensive book was preserved by the Arabs during the so-called "Dark Ages" that followed the fall of Rome; it was translated into Latin in the twelfth century and became, for the Middle Ages, the basic authority on astronomy.

7. Summary

In concluding this chapter on Greek science let us briefly summarize the achievements of these remarkable people. The Greeks invented critical philosophy and for the first time created an intellectual life. We owe to them the conception of impersonal law and the distinction between appearance and reality. They developed the art of reasoning and began a critical discussion of the meaning of words. To them we owe the first example of a logically constructed science: geometry worked out as a sequence of theorems based on a few primary axioms. Their contributions during the Alexandrian period to observational and theoretical astronomy were very great. Their attempts to deal with physics, chemistry, and biology were less successful, but in these fields also their observations and speculations were by no means unimportant.

Greek science admittedly had its serious weaknesses. The Greeks were the first in the field and inevitably fumbled for lack of experience. The early Greek philosophers tackled the most difficult problems without tools for dealing with them. They did not realize the need for building up knowledge bit by bit through patient observation and experimentation. Greek success in geometry produced an undue reliance on self-evident axioms as guides to scientific thinking. The Greeks were nearer than we to the primitive animistic view of nature that attributes every natural event to the will of some spirit. Although they developed the idea of impersonal law, they frequently failed to make the sharp distinction that we usually make between mechanical behavior and the purposeful behavior of living organisms. The preoccupation of Socrates and Plato with moral questions introduced a misleading twist into Greek physical science.

But, regardless of these scientific weaknesses, it is abundantly clear that the Greek stage in the evolution of human thought was a magnificent and necessary forerunner of the scientific age in which we live.

CHAPTER 2

The Copernican Revolution; the First Stage

For seven or eight centuries Greek culture dominated the Mediterranean world. It is our great heritage from the past, the base on which our modern culture is built. Unfortunately the Romans, who gained political control of the Mediterranean about 200 B.C., had a different scale of values. They were practical empire builders with only a casual interest in natural law and philosophy. They took over the schools started by the Greeks and much of Greek culture, but they did not maintain a vigorous intellectual life. As the Roman empire in turn went into its long period of decline, Christianity spread and came to dominate the disintegrating civilized world. It brought with it new hope for the common people and a new sense of personal dignity. But the early Church, fighting for its life against the pagan civilization of Rome, was even less interested in science and letters than non-Christian Rome had been. The Church fathers sought to save men from a corrupt civilization by directing their attention away from the world about them toward God and the life after death. They looked for the end of the world in the year 1000. In A.D. 390 a Christian bishop, Theophilus, destroyed a part of the great library at Alexandria. The Moslems, in 640, completed the destruction. The historian Sir William Dampier has described this event as one of the greatest intellectual catastrophes in history.

When the Roman Empire was overrun by barbarians in the fifth century, the Church did what it could to assimilate and civilize the invaders but could not prevent the onset of a long period of anarchy and economic misery. Science and learning all but disappeared in western Europe. Only the Byzantine Empire of the East maintained a civilization worthy of the name.

Typical of the point of view of the more enlightened elements of society in the West was the philosophy of St. Augustine (A.D. 354–430) in which Christianity was joined with mystical conceptions derived from Plato and the Pythagoreans. To the faithful he gave the advice, "Go not out of doors. Return into thyself. In the inner

1. Rome and the Dark Ages

man dwells truth."[1] Although the Church required schools for the training of her priests, liberal and scientific studies were frowned upon.

Fortunately, many of the documents of ancient Greek science were preserved at Byzantium and thence transmitted to the brilliant Islamic culture of the tenth, eleventh, and twelfth centuries. In Europe, Christian monasteries kept alive the arts of reading and writing. They also preserved a few of the documents of secular learning, but these dusty manuscripts could not battle the unchecked growth of superstition and credulity.

2. The Revival of Learning in the Middle Ages

The revival of learning in Europe during the twelfth, thirteenth, and fourteenth centuries was due in large part to Moslem influence. After the invasion of Europe by the Moslems in the seventh century, a more or less stable front was established dividing Christian Europe on the north from the Mohammedan–Arabian empire bordering the Mediterranean. Contacts established across this frontier, especially in Spain and southern Italy, allowed Christian scholars to rediscover the culture of ancient Greece. By the beginning of the twelfth century the principal works of Aristotle and Ptolemy had been translated from Arabic versions into Latin, the common language of the churchmen and scholars of the Middle Ages. At about this time the Church, now adopting a more liberal attitude toward learning, began to establish universities. Stable communities of teachers and students grew up at Salerno and Bologna in Italy, at Paris, in Cambridge, and at Salamanca in Spain. By the middle of the thirteenth century they had created the means and the incentives needed for a revival of learning.

In the thirteenth century, the Age of Faith and high point of the unified Church-dominated medieval society, there was a further change in attitude toward Greek science. Scholars of the Church examined Aristotle carefully, and this examination led to the integration of a large part of Aristotelean science into Christian theology. The resulting closely knit and logically consistent body of theological and physical doctrine forged by Albertus Magnus and St. Thomas Aquinas is called *scholastic philosophy*. Through the general acceptance of this philosophy, a modified Aristoteleanism became the authoritative science of the period.

The spherical, earth-centered universe of Eudoxus and Aristotle was beautifully adapted to the Christian conception of the divine plan that shapes human destiny. In this view, man's lower nature tends to drag him down to the abode of Satan in a hell, located by scholastic philosophy at the center of the earth beneath our feet. Man's higher nature, on the other hand, seeks union with God in a heaven in the fixed empyrean beyond the whirling sphere of the stars. The spheres between earth and heaven are the abode of angels and archangels who have charge of the movements of the celestial bodies. Both Aristotle and the scholastics drew a sharp distinction between the physics of the terrestrial, or sublunary, universe and the physics — if, indeed, the word is applicable — of

---

[1] See the description of the decline of science under the Romans and the rise of neoplatonic mysticism in Charles Singer, *A Short History of Science* (Clarendon Press, Oxford, 1941), from which the above quotation is taken.

the celestial spheres surrounding it. On earth we have gross, corruptible matter subject to perpetual change and forever seeking to reach the lowest possible level. The changeless, incorruptible heavens are made of a different substance to which the rules of terrestrial physics do not apply. And so it was made to appear that the architecture of the universe — Aristotle's architecture — is an expression of the divine plan for the salvation of man.

This development, described in detail in Dante's *Divine Comedy*, placed the cosmology and physics of Aristotle in a well-nigh impregnable position, but it did not wholly smother scientific activity. Critical scholarship in the fields of philosophy and science began to appear as early as the eleventh century and continued to the time of Copernicus. The activity was directed primarily at removal of inconsistencies in the inherited patterns of philosophy and science, but it was useful in preparing the way for more radical changes to come.

3. The Italian Renaissance and Nicolaus Copernicus

The Italian Renaissance may be said to date from the temporary cultural breakdown brought about by the horrors of the Great Plague of the fourteenth century. As society recovered from this blow, new forces began to be apparent. Indignation over corruption in the Church was preparing the way for the Protestant Reformation. Fresh interest in pagan humanism, in art and in nature, was fostered by a wealth of new manuscripts, many of them in the original Greek, that found their way into Europe at this time. A growing resistance to the overrigidity of scholastic philosophy could be felt. It was a period of economic advance and political change.

Interest in astronomy revived and was focused on two different problems. One of these was the need for reconciling the epicycles of Ptolemy's *Almagest* with the concentric spheres of Aristotle. To bring these conceptions together, the epicycles in the mathematics of Ptolemy were transformed by some authors into small spheres rolling between large spheres concentric or eccentric to the earth. The other problem arose from the fact that neither the original theory of Ptolemy nor any of its numerous Arabic modifications was adequate to fit all the observations available in the fifteenth century. Theory patching was the order of the day.

It was into this world of flux and scientific frustration that Nicolaus Copernicus was born, in 1473. He was a Polish monk favored with a prolonged education at the universities at Cracow in Poland, and at Bologna, Rome, Padua, and Ferrara in Italy.[2] While in Italy studying theology, law, medicine, mathematics, and astronomy he came into contact with leading astronomers and had the opportunity to hear professional discussion of the Ptolemaic system and the medieval attempts to revise and harmonize it with the cosmology of Aristotle. Here he may first have heard of the hitherto rejected ideas of Heracleides and Aristarchus and conceived the plan to bring order and simplicity into astronomy by transferring the center of the universe from the earth to the sun.

[2] For a readable account of the life of Copernicus see Angus Armitage, *Copernicus: The Founder of Modern Astronomy* (Doubleday and Co., Garden City, N.Y., 1962).

Presumably, when he returned to his native diocese and state of Ermland in Poland, he had this ambitious project very much on his mind. Installed as canon of the cathedral at Frauenberg and private physician to his aged uncle and patron, the Bishop of Ermland, Copernicus helped to govern the little state for six years, until the death of his uncle in 1512. In that year he distributed to friends a preliminary pamphlet called the *Little Commentary*, describing the main features of his new astronomical theory.

Copernicus was a many-sided man who lived an active life and was no scientific recluse. Although he was the parent of an unparalleled scientific and intellectual revolution, he was a man of his own time. His mind was saturated with the Pythagorean–Platonic mysticism so widespread in the Middle Ages. Besides being a monk and astronomer he was a physician, a manager of estates, an economist, and a man who found time to translate Greek verses into Latin prose. But in spite of many interests and duties he made numerous astronomical observations and was at pains to work out the details of his heliocentric system to see whether it could be fitted accurately to all the astronomical facts. In this investigation it was his purpose to reconcile all recorded data old and new, even though this involved him in difficult questions of chronology in fixing the true dates of the observations used by Ptolemy. The full account of the theory was finally embodied in an epoch-making book, *De Revolutionibus Orbium Cælestium*.

Evidently Copernicus was in no hurry to convert the world to his point of view, for the story is that the first copy of the book was finally brought to him on his deathbed, in 1543. This was more than 30 years after the appearance of the *Little Commentary*.

The long delay in publication was due in part to the fact that Copernicus expected severe criticism and hesitated to project himself into unpleasant controversy. In part the delay was due also, no doubt, to the laborious nature of the calculations needed to finish his work. The theory was much more than a bright idea. To fit the data it was necessary to resort to cumbersome complexities similar in kind to those of Ptolemy. Many numerical magnitudes had to be chosen, and many wrong guesses had inevitably to be tried out through months of detailed computation, only to be discarded in the end.

4. The Copernican Theory

4.1. The Basic Assumptions. We have described the fundamental ideas of the Copernican theory in Sec. 5 of Chap. 3. Copernicus assumed that the sun and stars are at rest, that the earth rotates about its axis of spin once every sidereal day and revolves about the sun once a year. He assumed also that the other planets revolve about the sun in orbits that never get far from the plane of the ecliptic and with the same direction of rotation as the earth's. The speeds of the planets are required to decrease as their distances from the sun increase. As a consequence, of course, the periods of rotation increase with distance from the sun. The moon alone revolves about the earth itself.

Copernicus would have liked to assume that all these are uniform circular motions, with the sun at the common center of all orbits except the moon's. The data are by no means in satisfactory agreement with this last hypothesis, but it does yield a useful first approximation. Using this approximation, Copernicus could develop a simplified heliocentric theory that explained the qualitative behavior of the planets much more elegantly than any corresponding simplification of the Ptolemaic theory. It will be convenient to discuss the simplified theory first, reserving for later consideration the complexities that must be added to fit the data quantitatively.

4.2. The Simplified Theory. Figure 4–1 will serve to illustrate the Copernican conception of the true motion of the earth and the planets. In this diagram the plane of the paper is the plane of the ecliptic, on which the orbital paths are projected. The sun and stars being at rest, the direction of the vernal equinox can be used as a fixed reference line. To make connections between such a diagram and the sun and planets as we see them, one must bear in mind one obvious fact: The apparent position of any member of the solar system projected against the distant background of stars is determined by the direction of the sight line drawn from the momentary position of the earth to the momentary position of the body in question.

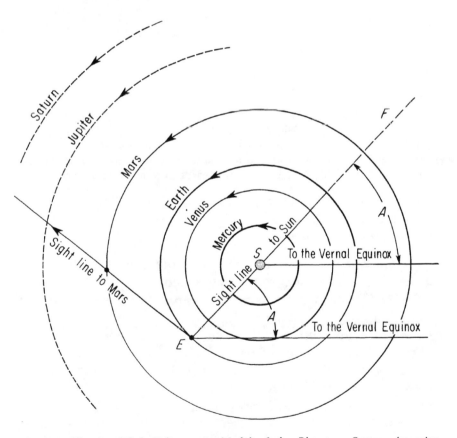

Fig. 4–1. *The Simplified Heliocentric Model of the Planetary System Assuming Concentric Circular Orbits.* In this figure the orbits of Mercury, Venus, Earth, and Mars are given their correct relative dimensions. The orbits of Jupiter and Saturn, however, are arbitrarily reduced to bring them into the diagram. If the earth is at *E*, the sun at *S* is projected against the distant background of stars along the sightline *ESF*. The angle *A* between the direction of the vernal equinox and the direction of the sun as seen from the earth is called the *celestial longitude* of the sun.

In discussing the work of Aristarchus (Chap. 3) we introduced the same simplified heliocentric theory by way of the intermediate hypothesis that the planets Mercury, Venus, Mars, Jupiter, and Saturn all revolve about the sun, which in turn revolves about the earth. The relative motions of the different heavenly bodies for the simplified heliocentric theory and the intermediate theory are the same. Since the intermediate theory gives a qualitative explanation of retrograde motions and variations in brightness of the planets, the fixed-sun theory must provide similar qualitative explanations. Figure 4–2 shows directly the heliocentric explanation of retrograde motion for an inferior planet. The same diagram can be used to make the corresponding demonstration for a superior planet if we think of the planet as moving on the outer circle and the earth on the inner one.

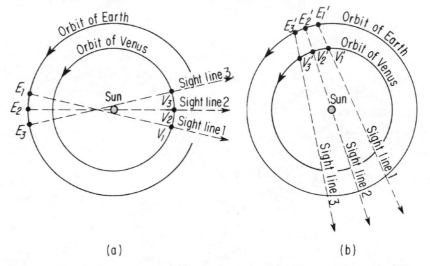

Fig. 4–2. *The Heliocentric Explanation of Retrograde Motion.* Diagram *a* shows three successive positions of the earth and three corresponding positions of Venus near the point of superior conjunction. Because Venus and the earth are on opposite sides of the sun and circulate around the sun in the counterclockwise sense, both motions help to tilt the sight line from the earth to Venus counterclockwise. At superior conjunction Venus overtakes the sun.

Diagram *b* shows a similar succession of positions of the earth and Venus 9.6 months later, when Venus has gained a half revolution on the earth and is in the position of inferior conjunction.

4.3. Sidereal Periods. In order to bring out more fully the beauty of the simplified theory, let us next consider the relation between the *synodic period* of each planet (cf. Chap. 2, Sec. 9) and its *sidereal period*. The *sidereal period* is defined as the time required for a planet to rotate once around the sun, when the sun and stars are taken as the basic frame of reference, as in Fig. 4–2. The *synodic period*, on the other hand, is the time that elapses between one moment of maximum retrograde motion and the next. Maximum retrograde motion of an inferior planet occurs at alternate conjunctions, that is, when the planet is passing the earth. Hence, the synodic period of such a planet is the time required for the planet to *gain* one revolution on the earth. Maximum retrograde motion of a superior planet occurs at points of opposition to the sun when the earth is passing the planet. The synodic period is in this case the time required for the planet to *lose* one revolution relative to the earth. In either case the synodic period is a directly observable time,[3] whereas the sidereal period is not. We have to compute the sidereal periods from the synodic periods.

Consider the motion of an inferior planet, either Venus or Mercury. Assume as before that it rotates more rapidly than the earth. Denote the sidereal periods of the earth and the planet in question by T_E and T_P, respectively. Let S be the synodic period of the planet. In unit time the earth makes $1/T_E$ revolutions about the sun. Therefore, in the time S it must make S/T_E revolutions. In the same time the planet must make S/T_P revolutions. But from the definition of S the number of revolutions of the planet in this time *exceeds* the number of revolutions of the earth by unity. Hence,

$$\frac{S}{T_P} - \frac{S}{T_E} = 1. \tag{4.1}$$

Solving this equation for T_P we obtain:

$$\text{Sidereal period inferior planet} = T_P = \frac{ST_E}{S + T_E}. \tag{4.2}$$

In the case of a superior planet the number of revolutions of the earth in a synodic period (S/T_E) exceeds the number of revolutions of the planet (S/T_P) by unity. It follows then that:

$$\text{Sidereal period superior planet} = T_P = \frac{ST_E}{S - T_E}. \tag{4.3}$$

For the inferior planet Venus the mean synodic period is about 584 days. Its sidereal period is accordingly

$$T_P \text{ (Venus)} = \frac{584 \times 365.25}{584 + 365.25} = 225 \text{ days}. \tag{4.4}$$

For the superior planet Mars the mean synodic period is about 780 days. Its sidereal period is therefore

$$T_P \text{ (Mars)} = \frac{780 \times 365.25}{780 - 365.25} = 687 \text{ days}. \tag{4.5}$$

4.4. Relative Radii. We now proceed to work out the relative radii of the planetary orbits. These are defined as the ratios of the orbital radii to that of the earth. They are easily evaluated if we treat the orbits as concentric circles.

Consider first an inferior planet, say Venus. At the moment of maximum elongation (maximum angular separation from the sun) the line of sight from the earth to Venus (Fig. 4–3a) is tangent to the orbit of that planet and so perpendicular to the line joining Venus to the sun. So the triangle SEV is a right triangle; the relative radius SV/SE is equal to the trigonometric sine of the angle ϕ at E, which is easily measured. For Venus the average value of the angle is 47° and the corresponding relative radius is 0.73.

The procedure is a little more complicated for a superior planet. In this case one can observe the time when the planet is at right angles to the sun on the approach to opposition. The corresponding

---

[3] Due to the noncircular character of the true planetary orbits, the observed synodic periods are not exactly equal, but in the present calculation we use the mean observed period and ignore the inequalities.

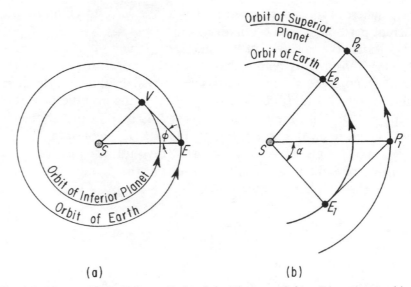

(a)   (b)

Fig. 4–3. *Measuring the Relative Radii of the Planetary Orbits.* Diagram *a*: orbit of inferior planet. Diagram *b*: orbit of superior planet.

positions of the earth and planet are then as indicated by the points E_1 and P_1 of Fig. 4–3b. After a certain time interval, say T, the earth will catch up with the planet, which will then be opposite to the sun. Earth and planet now occupy the positions E_2 and P_2 on the diagram. Since the angle between the sun and planet can be observed continuously, we can determine the times of the two relative positions and so measure the time interval T. During this time interval the angle between the earth and the planet as seen from the sun will have decreased from the initial value α to zero. The gain in angle per unit time is therefore α/T. But the gain in angle in a synodic period S is 360°. Since the gain in angle per unit time is constant, α/T must be equal to $360/S$. Thus the angle α is equal to $360T/S$. But Fig. 4–3b shows that the cosine of α is the reciprocal of the relative radius. This relationship makes it easy to work out the desired relative radius.

As it turned out, the relative radii evaluated in this way are related to the sidereal periods; the periods increase with the radii, as shown in Table 4.1. Figure 4–4 shows a plot of relative radius against sidereal period, using modern data. In this plot the orbital

Table 4.1. *Relative Orbital Radii and Sidereal Periods of the Planets*

| Planet | Relative Radius | | Period in Years |
	Copernicus*	Modern Value	Modern Value
Mercury	0.376	0.387	0.241
Venus	0.719	0.723	0.615
Earth	1.00	1.00	1.00
Mars	1.52	1.52	1.88
Jupiter	5.22	5.20	11.86
Saturn	9.17	9.54	29.46

* From J. L. E. Dreyer, *A History of Astronomy from Thales to Kepler* (Dover Publishing Co., New York, 1953), p. 339.

radius of each planet is taken as the ordinate of a point whose abscissa is the period of the same planet. Thus each planet is represented by a plotted point shown by a black spot. From the plot we see clearly what we can sense by inspection of the table: that the radii of the orbits are simply related to the corresponding periods, and the points can be joined by a smooth curve. The chance that the six points on the diagram are arranged in this manner by accident is obviously very small. If not the result of accident, the plot must be the expression of a general law. But such a law could make sense *only* if the quantities plotted on the basis of the calculations of Copernicus do in fact have the significance which his theory gave them. The period and radii are *not* the products of a disordered imagination!

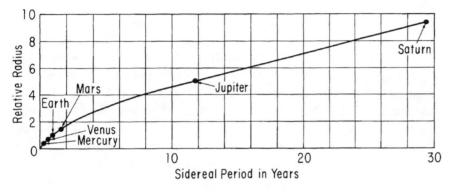

Fig. 4–4. *Relative Orbital Radius Plotted against Orbital Period.* The data used in drawing this graph are modern.

Thus the ordered relation between the computed radii and computed periods can be regarded as important evidence for the validity of the heliocentric theory — evidence that would never have come to light if the author of the theory had not taken the trouble to fill in the quantitative details of his conception by working out these numerical values.

So far as we know, Copernicus himself did not draw the curve of Fig. 4–4, but he did realize that the planets can be put into an ordered sequence in which orbital periods and orbital radii progress together. He also realized that *the earth fits into this sequence and must be regarded as a member of the complete family of planets* — a great triumph for his point of view because it greatly simplifies the whole astronomic picture.

4.5. The Complicated Final Theory. When the orbital periods and radii were worked out, the simplified form of the Copernican theory was essentially complete. But unfortunately this simplified theory, though qualitatively satisfactory, did not fit the observational facts with sufficient accuracy to be useful for the prediction of the details of the motion of the planets. So Copernicus felt compelled to resort to the introduction of epicycles and eccentrics to convert the simplified theory into an instrument for quantitative prediction, like Ptolemy's theory. Since the radius, period, and phase of the motion on each new circle were adjusted to the data, the extra circles gave flexibility to the scheme. But the number of circles required was suspiciously large. The final theory seemed about as complicated as that of Ptolemy. The earth itself was made to move on a large primary circle, eccentric to the sun, whose center revolves on a second circle, whose center revolves on a third, sun-centered circle! In all, Copernicus used some 34 circles where contemporary versions of the Ptolemaic theory used nearly 80. He failed to achieve real simplicity and still was not able to fit the observations perfectly.

5. Scientific Theories and How to Judge Them

5.1. A Theory is an Explanation. Copernicus substituted a new theory for an old one. To judge the merits of his performance we need to pause for a little reflection about theories in general, especially scientific theories. What do we mean by a theory? What are theories good for? How are we to discriminate between good theories and poor ones?

The dictionaries say that a theory is an explanation. It is in fact an interpretation of observations or experiences that fits them into the general pattern of our thought or organizes them by showing that they are tied together by one or more broad general principles. A scientific theory is concerned with a range of related facts or observations that have scientific standing because they have been scrutinized and accredited by trained and trustworthy observers. It organizes and explains the facts or observations in terms of a mutually consistent set of ideas and assumptions. From a logical point of view a theory ideally should consist of two distinct parts: the basic definitions and assumptions which are its core, and the logical fabric of deduced consequences. This ideal structure is beautifully exemplified in Euclidean geometry, with its precisely stated axioms, theorems, and corollaries. But physical theories, whose assumptions are suggested by experimental facts, are commonly built up piecemeal. Hence, the presentation of such theories rarely sticks to the ideal logical form.

The general principles on which a scientific theory is erected are usually *not* of a kind that can be verified directly by observation. For this reason we commonly make a sharp distinction between statements of fact and statements wholly or partially based on theory. Theoretical statements are viewed with confidence or skepticism, depending on the standing of the theory.

The Ptolemaic theory can serve as an example. In this theory the stars were *assumed* to occupy places on a giant sphere that rotates like a rigid body about the earth's polar axis. The sun was *assumed* to revolve around the earth on a slightly eccentric circular orbit, and the planets were *assumed* to move with a combination of uniform circular motions on epicycles and deferents. None of these assumptions was directly verifiable. Taken together they provided the basis for a description of a total motion in three-dimensional space reasonably consistent with observations made from the surface of the earth.

Most human thinking is based on theories of one kind or another. Theories are, so to speak, all about us; the germ theory of disease, the wave theory of light, the theory of airplane design, the atomic theory of matter, Freud's theory of the influence of the subconscious mind on human behavior, the astrologists' theory of the influence of the planets and stars on human destiny, Karl Marx's economic theory of history. Some of these theories are of the highest merit; others have a lower rating. Only astrology stands out among them as an ancient delusion wholly without warrant from a scientific point of view. Our civilization is based on many theories of one kind and another, for theories are the guides by which we design our machines and order our conduct.

Theories differ enormously among themselves in scope, in precision of formulation, in degree of elaboration, and in what we call the "level of abstraction" involved in their assumptions. If the ideas used in a theory are easy to comprehend because they appeal to our intuition or make connections with everyday experience, we say that the theory has a "low level of abstraction." The germ theory of disease and the Ptolemaic theory of astronomy, for example, fall in this class. But if, as in Einstein's theory of relativity, the ideas involved are difficult because they are remote from daily experience, we say the theory has a "high level of abstraction."

Unfortunately for the would-be scientist, the theories of modern physical science tend to be very abstract. One reason for this tendency is that the most powerful and important theories are those that have a broad range of applications. But conceptions that are applicable in a wide variety of concrete situations must be based on the process of picking out common elements from many specific cases. Such conceptions are abstract by definition. They are inventions of the creative imagination of the scientist and have little appeal to the intuition of the ordinary layman.

5.2. The Value of a Theory. Let us return at this point to the problem of judging the merits of a scientific theory. From the standpoint of the modern scientist we may say that a good theory can be valuable for four principal reasons:

(a) A good theory provides a convenient mental picture or mathematical structure that enables the mind to grasp a variety of otherwise unrelated or slightly related facts. By organizing information it helps us to remember and use it.

(b) A good theory provides a basis for the prediction of the outcome of various experiments, observations, and courses of action. It is therefore a guide to the solution of practical problems, whether of engineering, medicine, psychiatry, or politics. Of particular importance are the applications of improved theories in any one science to problems that confront other sciences: for example, the application of physical theory to astronomy, or of chemical theory to biology.

(c) A good theory points out unsuspected relations between previously observed facts and suggests new relations to be tested by additional observations. In answering some questions it raises a host of others. It is not a dead end but the beginning of a new chapter of investigations. Experience shows that scientific understanding tends to grow like a vigorous and healthy organism. In this growth each important new and valid insight stimulates the minds of all workers in the field and leads to a surge of exceptionally rapid progress.

(d) Finally, a good scientific theory can be a source of intense mental satisfaction to the scientific worker. It is an insight into the permanent order of the universe, a basis for understanding what is going on, and, because it can be used to predict and plan, a source of power. Since our minds are attuned to order and simplicity, a good theory has a strong aesthetic appeal. It reveals what is immutable and trustworthy in a world of changing appearances.

To those who have shared in its development, the formulation of such a theory means success in meeting a challenge of a high order, set by nature herself.

5.3. The Greek and Modern Views Compared. The point of view of the early Greeks regarding scientific theory, it must be emphasized, was quite different from the modern one described in the foregoing paragraphs. They believed that the universe is governed by broad philosophic principles intelligible to the human mind—for example, the principle of the superiority of uniform circular motion. To account for phenomena in broad general terms by appealing to such principles without bothering about quantitative details was to achieve an aesthetically harmonious view of the universe. From this point of view we can understand the appeal of a chemical theory which assumed that all matter is composed in varying proportions of earth, water, air, and fire but gave no clear idea of the difference between a chemical compound and a mixture.

The Greeks intended their theories to lay bare the *reality* behind the world of appearance. They classified theories as *true* or *false* according to whether they correctly described reality or failed to do so. Unfortunately the Greeks overestimated the importance of plausible broad general principles as criteria of truth and underestimated the importance of detailed study of the facts of observation. They could not foresee the power of a scientific method that had not been invented, nor could they have conceived the way in which the use of this method would eventually modify our understanding of the terms *reality* and *truth*.

By contrast, the scientist of today in the discussion of his theories uses the words *truth* and *reality* with caution. In a sense, he is as deeply devoted to the search for truth as anyone can be. But he has become somewhat skeptical of absolute truth and tends to concentrate his attention on the attainment of a verifiable and practically useful understanding of the physical and biological universe in which he lives. In the domain of science this developing understanding becomes the best available substitute for ultimate truth, which seems beyond the reach of the scientist.

The history of science shows that scientific understanding grows by the use of a succession of theories, each improving on its predecessors, each built on those concepts available at the time of its construction that best lend themselves to a simple, harmonious, and relatively complete description of the known facts of observation. Looking back from the mid-twentieth century over the wreckage of once-valuable scientific theories that are no longer adequate expressions of our advancing knowledge, the scientist can hardly avoid questioning the permanence of *any* scientific theory. Clearly, a theory whose value is temporary, or one of limited scope, cannot be regarded as a correct description of reality, or final truth.

If one asks why it is that so often scientific theories gain high standing at one time, only to be discarded in the years that follow, the answer is not far to seek. We test a scientific theory by comparing its predictions with the available experimental facts. If these facts agree with the theory within the range of the inevitable experimental errors, the theory gains a limited confirmation and acquires scientific standing. If a theory survives such tests a presumption is created that it will survive further tests of the same kind. It acquires predictive value. The tests never suffice, however, to show that the assumptions on which the theory is based are absolutely and unqualifiedly correct. The observations are always finite in number and rarely can cover the complete range of possible values of the physical quantities involved. They can never prove that new observations taken over a wider range of conditions or made with improved accuracy will not reveal discrepancies that require a modification of the theory, or force the adoption of a radically different conceptual scheme.

From another point of view one can say that if a given theory fits any finite set of experimental data, it must also be possible to construct many other theories that fit the same data. So it is always possible that more information will require a different selection among the many theoretical possibilities. Experimental tests can show negatively that a theoretical principle is false; they can never provide a final positive test for its truth.

In the absence of a satisfactory test for ultimate truth, the famous American psychologist and philosopher William James went so far as to propose that for philosophic and scientific purposes we discard the notion of ultimate, or absolute, truth and identify the truth of a theory in a relative way, with its success as an interpretation of our experience. To put it crudely, his point of view was that we should identify truth with ideas and conceptions that "work." This philosophic conception originated in discussions between William James and Charles S. Peirce. The doctrine is known as *pragmatism.*

The caution of the scientist about accepting scientific theories as glimpses of the reality behind the world of appearance sounds like extreme scientific pessimism. The situation is not, however, as bad as this statement by itself might seem to imply. A scientific theory achieves status only when it has been found valid to a reasonable degree of accuracy within a certain range of application. When such a theory has been displaced by a new theory of broader range and greater power it has nearly always been true that important features of the old theory were preserved in the new. In fact this must be so, for the experimentally testable relations, such as Boyle's law for gases or Galileo's law for falling bodies, that are successfully predicted by the old theory, must also be predicted by the new theory if it is to challenge the old one successfully. For this reason the history of scientific theories shows that the gains made by each generation of scientists are substantially preserved in the next. Therefore, scientists have a justified sense of a growing understanding of the physical universe. From this point of view it would seem that science does progressively distinguish between appearance and reality.

5.4. Criteria of Excellence. On the basis of our practical interpretation of the value of theories we can proceed to formulate a series of specific criteria that will help us to judge their merits.

(*a*) *The assumptions of a good theory should be consistent with the well-established facts in the area of applicability of the theory.*

As James B. Conant has pointed out, this familiar criterion should not be interpreted to mean that one small fact in conflict with a theory must necessarily throw it into immediate discard. On the contrary, the usefulness of a theory in the organization of knowledge and as a guide to the solution of practical problems is likely to continue, despite some discrepancies, until a better theory has been worked out. Only the appearance of a new theory that more completely fits the facts can drive the old one out of use.

(*b*) *A theory should be as simple as possible. In particular, the number of independent assumptions used should be small in comparison with the range of facts accounted for.*

Clearly a theory cannot organize knowledge if it is as complicated as the factual data. If every fact is accounted for by a corresponding assumption, the explanation can have no value whatever. But it should be understood that the requirement of simplicity does not demand a low level of abstraction. The basic theories of modern physics are very abstract; they make little appeal to common sense and are hard to grasp. We retain them nevertheless, because of their enormous success in organizing knowledge, in exact prediction, and in stimulating new experimental work.

(*c*) *A good theory in the physical sciences is preferably quantitative.*

To be quantitative is to be exact. Only an exact theory can make exact predictions. Moreover, only a quantitative theory can be subjected to stringent tests. A purely qualitative theory is almost impossible to confirm or refute. In the area of physical science, where quantitative theories are possible, a qualitative theory can be useful only as a starting point for the construction of a quantitative one. In other areas, however, qualitative theories can be of major importance.

(*d*) *A good theory should have a broad range of application.*

The mechanical theory of Newton, to cite an illustrative example, is valid, as we shall see later, for the discussion of the motion of bodies large enough to be seen without a microscope, moving at speeds that are small in comparison with that of light. Its range of application is small in comparison with relativistic quantum mechanics, a modern theory applicable to the same bodies and motions as the Newtonian theory and in addition to submicroscopic particles and to the highest speeds that can be observed. Of course, quantum mechanics is given the higher rating

(*e*) *A good theory tends to suggest new facts and relations for investigation, thus preparing the way for further experimental and theoretical discoveries.*

Finally, it should be noted that *the merit of a theory* is demonstrated and its value to society enhanced when it leads to advances in the solution of socially important technological problems. Of course, the inherent significance of a theory as a contribution to pure science is independent of such applications.

In conclusion, it will be well to note that the foregoing criteria of scientific excellence do not by themselves determine whether or not a sweeping theory, such as that of Ptolemy or that of Copernicus, will be quickly accepted. Scientific theories, like social reforms, have to meet philosophic preconceptions in the minds of scientists and others. If a theory is to gain quick recognition, it must make sense to the average hearer. In other words, it must harmonize with the broad assumptions regarding the nature of the universe that are usually taken for granted among the educated people of the time — the assumptions that make up what is sometimes called "the philosophy of common sense." Experience shows that, in practice, the acceptance of a broad and important scientific theory can be seriously delayed if it is in conflict with common sense or with a widely held religious or political philosophy. In the long run the success of a scientific theory is usually based on purely scientific considerations. Philosophy eventually adjusts itself to the proper demands of science. In the beginning, however, a revolutionary scientific theory in conflict with the prevailing current of philosophic thought is sure to meet strong opposition.

6. The Relative Merits of the Ptolemaic and Copernican Theories

Comparing the Ptolemaic and Copernican theories in the light of the criteria listed in the foregoing section, we note that both are quantitative and that in their ability to represent the existing data there was little to choose between them.[4] The range of application was nearly the same.

The great advantage of the Copernican system lay in the interpretive power of the elementary form of the theory. For Copernicus both the oscillations superposed on the forward movements of the planets and their variations in brightness were illusions caused by the fact that we see them from a revolving platform. His theory provided a physical explanation for the observed correlation between the apparent motion of the sun and the apparent motions of the planets. This explanation gave the theory a positive content and interpretive power which the Ptolemaic theory lacked because it set up an arbitrary independent mechanism for each individual planet.

The fact is that in each case the maximum retrograde motion and the maximum forward motion of a planet occur when the planet, the earth, and the sun are in the same straight line. The Copernican theory explains why, but the Ptolemaic theory does not. In the latter theory this connection between the behavior of each planet and the position of the sun is an unexplained accident. It is also a fact that the retrograde motions are largest for those planets, Mars and Venus, whose orbits come closest to the earth. Only the Copernican theory gave an explanation of this fact. Therefore, the Copernican theory did a better job of organizing the facts than the Ptolemaic theory did.

---

[4] In speaking of the Ptolemaic theory we here refer not to the one theory described in the *Almagest* but to the dozen or more modifications proposed by Islamic and medieval European astronomers. Cf. T. S. Kuhn, *The Copernican Revolution* (Harvard University Press, Cambridge, Mass., 1957), pp. 138–139.

A second major advantage of the Copernican theory is to be found in the way in which the earth's orbit about the sun fits into the family of planetary orbits. In the data of Table 4.1 and the plot of Fig. 4–4 we have seen a previously unsuspected relationship between the periods and the calculated relative radii that cannot be accidental, a relationship completely covered up by the Ptolemaic interpretations of the data.

Copernicus himself, a firm believer in uniform circular motions, took pride in his success in eliminating Ptolemy's equants, which seemed to him gross violations of the uniform-circular-motion principle. He laid great stress on the harmonious geometry of the heavens which his system revealed. He clung to the conception of real celestial spheres, but centered them on the sun. His mystical, neoplatonic outlook[5] is clearly evident in a famous passage from *De Revolutionibus*:

In the middle of all sits Sun enthroned. In this most beautiful temple could we place this luminary in any better position from which he can illuminate the whole at once? He is rightly called the Lamp, the Mind, the Ruler of the Universe; Hermes Trismegistus names him the Visible God, Sophocles' Electra calls him the All-seeing. So the Sun sits upon a royal throne ruling his children, the planets which circle round him. The Earth has the Moon at her service. As Aristotle says,... the moon has the closest relationship with the Earth. Meanwhile the Earth conceives by the Sun, and becomes pregnant with an annual rebirth.

So we find underlying this ordination an admirable symmetry in the Universe, and a clear bond of harmony in the motion and magnitude of the spheres such as can be discovered in no other wise. For here we may observe why the progression and retrogression appear greater for Jupiter than Saturn, and less than for Mars, but again greater for Venus than in Mercury; moreover, why Saturn, Jupiter, and Mars are nearer to the Earth at opposition to the Sun than when they are lost in or emerge from the Sun's rays.... All these phenomena proceed from the same cause namely Earth's motion.[6]

Unfortunately Copernicus found it difficult to make the advantages of his theory entirely clear to his readers. The addition of many moving eccentrics and epicycles in the final theory obscured the fundamental simplicity of the heliocentric scheme.[7] Because the physics of the Middle Ages was the physics of Aristotle, the arguments of the ancient Greeks against the idea of a moving earth were still effective. With respect to physics Copernicus had not escaped from the medieval view; his efforts to justify his theory from a physical point of view were unsuccessful. He did not live to carry on an extended debate with his critics; the book he left behind was mathematical and obscure.

[5] See Herbert Butterfield, *The Origins of Modern Science* (G. Bell & Sons, London, 1950), Chap. 2; T. S. Kuhn, *op. cit.*, Chap. 5. Kuhn gives extensive quotations from *De Revolutionibus*.

[6] This quotation is from the translation of *De Revolutionibus* by Dobson and Brodetsky published as *Occasional Notes of the Royal Astronomical Society*, Vol. 2, No. 10 (Royal Astronomical Society, London, 1947).

[7] Copernicus has been criticized for including some obviously faulty observations with the good in the data he attempted to fit. This error made his task more difficult and contributed to the final complexity of his theory.

7.1. Initial Reactions; Bruno. It is not surprising in the circumstances that the theory of Copernicus was received with little warmth by the astronomers and attracted little attention outside the scientific circle. Approval and violent opposition were both slow in developing. Copernicus was a highly respected churchman. His work was primarily technical and his attitude toward theology in no sense revolutionary: *De Revolutionibus* was dedicated to Pope Paul III. The preface was written by a Lutheran minister, Andreas Osiander, who cautiously represented the heliocentric hypothesis as a mathematical device for the convenience of astronomers rather than as a new conception of the actual nature of the universe. In the beginning Catholic scholars received the book with singular open-mindedness. Criticism from the Protestant camp was sharper but by no means unanimous.

The early liberalism of the Roman Church was not to continue, however. Copernicus was a conservative revolutionist; more radical views than his soon began to appear, and with them came a change in the attitude of the Church hierarchy. Copernicus made the earth move and brought the sun and stars to rest. He replaced the earth by the sun at the center of planetary motion and at the center of the sphere of the stars. But the universe remained, for him, a finite spherical universe not necessarily unacceptable from a theological point of view. What could not be accepted was the doctrine of the pantheist philosopher and renegade monk Giordano Bruno (1547–1600).

Bruno was not an astronomer but an iconoclastic thinker who accepted the Copernican heliocentric scheme with enthusiasm. He was one of the first to appreciate the fact that in bringing the sphere of the stars to rest, Copernicus had unwittingly destroyed the reason for believing in its existence. In the Aristotelean view the celestial sphere was a rigid rotating frame to which the stars were attached. Its existence explained the fact that, unlike the planets, they all seemed to move together. Its finite radius provided a needed limit to the stellar velocities. But if the stars do not rotate there is nothing to prevent us from assuming that they are scattered through infinite space. The earth, moon, and planets shine by reflected light, but, since the stars are visible at enormously greater distances, it seemed to Bruno that they must be self-luminous like the sun. He wandered over Europe from university to university, teaching that the stars are suns spread through infinite space, each surrounded by whirling planets inhabited, perhaps, by living creatures like ourselves. If the earth is not the center of the universe, said Bruno, why should we think of the sun as the center? An infinite universe has no center. If the universe is infinite in size, why not infinite in time?

So Bruno turned away from Christianity to pantheism. To a generation whose hopes and fears had been firmly tied by Thomas Aquinas to the neat, man-centered universe of Dante, such ideas were frightening. Bruno was burned at the stake in 1600.

7.2. Tycho Brahe. The strong hostility engendered by Bruno could be overcome only by fresh scientific evidence. To develop such evidence required time, but in time it was forthcoming—thanks primarily to the joint labors of four brilliant scientists: Tycho Brahe, Johannes Kepler, Galileo Galilei, and Isaac Newton. They carried on from the primitive beginning of Copernicus and proved that his basic assumption met the ultimate test of a great scientific conception—it had the capacity to stimulate imagination and open new doors.

If astronomy was to escape from the confusing complexities in which the brilliant insight of Copernicus had bogged down, its first great need was for improved observations and more of them. This need was supplied by the Danish astronomer Tycho Brahe, born in 1546, one year before Bruno and three years after the death of Copernicus. His royal patron, Frederick II of Denmark, being deeply interested in astrology, built a castle, Uraniborg, on the island of Hveen for Tycho to use as an observatory. There the astronomer watched the sky for 21 years until the death of Frederick. Unfortunately, Tycho had a habit of sarcastic speech that created powerful enemies; in 1597 they forced him into exile. In this extremity he sought refuge with a second royal patron, Emperor Rudolf II, in Bohemia. The astronomer died at Prague in 1601.

Tycho developed a variety of improved instruments and techniques for accurate naked-eye observations and accumulated a large fund of precise systematic data on the motion of the planets. By averaging a series of observations he was able to locate star positions with an uncertainty of less than one minute of arc. The positions of the moving planets could be fixed to about four minutes of arc.

Early in 1600, the year of the tragic martyrdom of Bruno, Tycho received a visit from Johannes Kepler, a gifted young Copernican astronomer with a flair for mathematics. He engaged him as his assistant, but they had only a year to work together before illness and death claimed the older man. To Kepler, Tycho bequeathed his precious store of data.

Tycho never accepted the Copernican hypothesis but introduced as a compromise the theory described in Chap. 3, Sec. 5.5, in which the planets Mercury, Venus, Mars, Jupiter, and Saturn all revolve about the sun, while the sun itself revolves about a fixed earth. So far as the observed motions are concerned, this Tychonic theory is an exact equivalent of the heliocentric theory. The two theories state the same facts in different languages based on different frames of reference. The difference between them is fundamentally not so much a matter of truth or falsity, as it is a matter of convenience, for which the heliocentric view is preferable because of its simplicity. We cannot describe motion without choosing a frame of reference, and any choice is necessarily as legitimate as any other.

When we go on to consider not only the geometry of the heavens but also the mechanical explanation of planetary motion in terms of the law of gravitation, and certain optical phenomena revealed by telescopic and spectroscopic analyses of starlight, we discover that the advantage of the Copernican frame of reference is very much greater than anyone could appreciate in the sixteenth

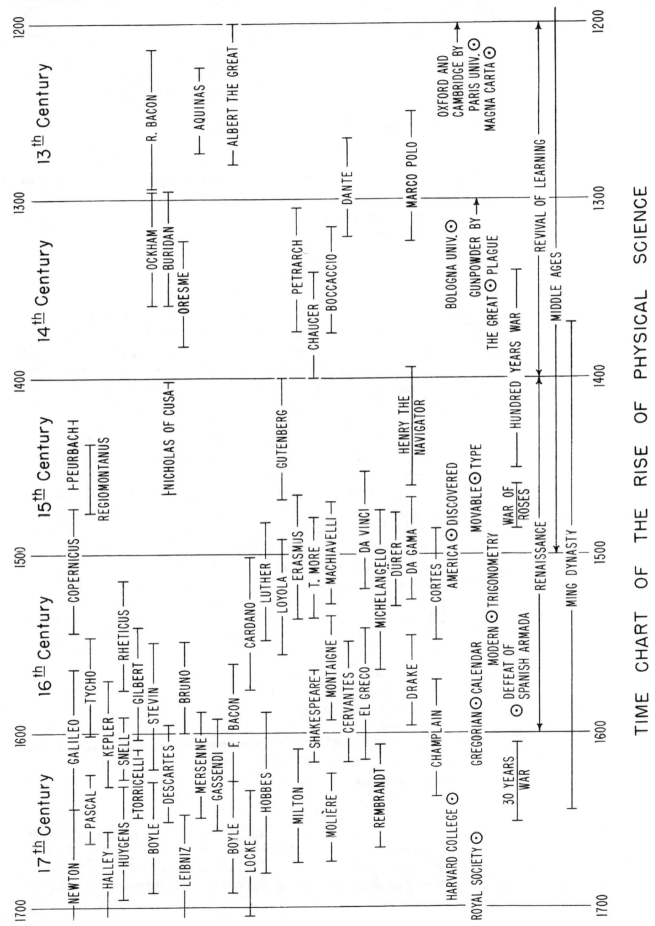

TIME CHART OF THE RISE OF PHYSICAL SCIENCE

century. It was through the insights made available by that frame of reference that the essential unity of the physics of terrestrial phenomena and the physics of the heavens was established. So we habitually think of the orbital motion of the earth around the sun as real and the apparent motion of the sun around the earth as an illusion. But even today astronomers have need of both the fixed-earth language — the language of their telescope settings — and the fixed-sun language in which the behavior of the solar system as a mechanical system is most easily understood.

In Tycho's time the issue was not interpreted as a matter of language but of truth, and he had it both ways, for his system accepted the traditional fixed-earth view as true but retained most of the simplicity of the Copernican theory, of which it was, in effect, a translation.

7.3. Kepler, the Man. Johannes Kepler (1571–1630), Tycho's scientific heir, was a mathematical and speculative genius very different from his master. In some respects Kepler is a rather tragic figure among the scientists of his time. He was subject to recurrent periods of ill health and beset throughout his life by financial and domestic worries. His lifelong ambition to work out a unified mechanical theory of the solar system ended in failure, and his great discoveries regarding the motions of the planets received scant attention throughout his life and for years thereafter.

For more than ten years following the death of Tycho, Kepler served as astronomer and mathematician to Emperor Rudolf. This appointment meant that the preparation of astrological almanacs was his official business. The *Rudolphine Tables* of planetary motions, begun at this time, occupied much of Kepler's attention until their final publication in 1627.

Kepler's mind, like that of Copernicus, was "rooted in a time when animism, alchemy, astrology, numerology, and witchcraft presented problems to be seriously argued."[8] Theology, philosophy, and science were equally the objects of his enthusiastic attention. His voluminous and candid writings tell the story of a long struggle to reconcile Pythagorean mysticism with a profound respect for exact quantitative measurements.

Aristotle's distinction between the physics of terrestrial motions and the physics of the heavens was retained by Copernicus but swept aside by Kepler. At an early date he accepted the Copernican point of view and conceived the idea of a unified solar system governed by a physical law of gravitation. He correctly attributed the ocean tides to the gravitational influence of the moon. He threw off the spell of superposed uniform circular motions cast over astronomy by Plato, some 2000 years earlier, and undertook the direct determination of the shapes of the planetary orbits in the Copernican frame of reference. His procedures were laborious and the computations were hampered by numerous arithmetical mistakes, but after many discouraging failures he reached his objective.

[8] The quotation is from Gerald Holton, "*Johannes Kepler's Universe: Its Physics and Metaphysics*", Am. J. Phys. *24*, 340 (1956).

7.4. Kepler's Laws. Kepler discovered three major laws about the motion of the planets in the Copernican frame of reference. They were to be the foundation on which Newton some 50 years later erected a rational explanation of the solar system. Kepler was not able to establish the full generality of these observational laws. Time and data were lacking for that. But he was the trail blazer, and the laws rightly bear his name today. Let us examine them briefly before going on to a consideration of the methods by which they were laid bare. They are:

1. *Every planet moves in an elliptic orbit with one focus at the sun.*
2. *The line joining the sun with any one of the planets sweeps over equal areas in equal intervals of time.*
3. *The ratio of the square of the sidereal period to the cube of the mean distance from the sun is the same for all the planets.*

We know today that all three laws actually apply to all bodies revolving about the sun, including the minor planets, or asteroids, and comets.

To clarify the first law we need to define an *ellipse*. It is a plane curve (Fig. 4–5) so drawn that the sum of the distances of a moving point Q on the curve from two fixed points F_1 and F_2, called the foci, remains constant. In other words, it is the locus of all points Q for which the sum of the distances QF_1 and QF_2 has a fixed value. A curve of this kind is easily drawn with a pencil pressed against a cord whose ends are attached to pins or pegs located at the desired foci.

Any curve of this class is a closed oval figure symmetrical with respect to the line F_1F_2 joining the foci and with respect to the perpendicular bisector of F_1F_2. The *major axis* of the ellipse is the diameter AP, obtained by extending the line joining the foci until it intersects the ellipse at two points A and P. The length of the major axis, designated as $2a$ is equal to the fixed sum of the distances QF_1 and QF_2. The *minor axis* is the perpendicular diameter MN.

The *eccentricity* e is the ratio of the distance between the foci to the length of the major axis. Hence, the distance from the center of the figure to either focus is ae. The half-length of the minor axis b is related to a and e by the equation

$$b^2 = a^2(1 - e^2). \tag{4.4}$$

If we keep the major axis (length of cord) fixed and pull the foci apart, they approach the ends of the major axis as limits and at the same time the minor axis approaches the value zero. Thus a straight line joining the ends of the major axis constitutes a kind of limiting special case in which the eccentricity e is unity. If, on the other hand, we keep a constant as before but allow e to approach the limiting value zero, the foci approach the center O, and the ellipse degenerates into a *circle* with O as its center. A third limiting case is obtained by holding points P and F_1 fixed and moving F_2 off to infinity. The open curve so defined is called a *parabola*.

In general the size of an ellipse can be considered fixed by its major axis, and its shape by the eccentricity e or the ratio of the axes b/a.

In view of Kepler's first law we can interpret the ellipse of Fig. 4–5 as a possible planetary orbit with the sun located at one of the foci, say F_1. In that case the points P and A at which the planet's distance from the sun is a minimum and maximum,

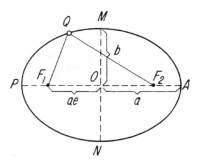

Fig. 4–5. *An Ellipse.* The sum of the distances QF_1 and QF_2 remains constant as Q moves around the curve.

respectively, are designated as the *perihelion* (near-sun) and *aphelion* (far-from-sun) points. The distances PF_1 and AF_1 are very different for a highly eccentric ellipse but approach equality as the eccentricity decreases toward zero. Actually the orbits of most of the major planets have quite low eccentricities, and consequently the circular orbit approximation of Secs. 4.3 and 4.4 works fairly well. The orbital eccentricities of the asteroids are frequently much larger. Some comets have closed orbits of large eccentricity while others, which have been seen but once, may be visitors from interstellar space moving in unclosed hyperbolic orbits that are created by an accidental encounter with the sun's gravitational field.

Figure 4–6 illustrates Kepler's second law. The equal-area rule implies that the linear speed of each planet increases as it approaches the sun and decreases again as it recedes from the sun.

The third law is the exact mathematical statement of the relation between relative radius and sidereal period, revealed by Table 4.1 and Fig. 4–4 in Sec. 4.4. The average distance between the planet and the sun mentioned in the law is to be identified with the semimajor axis a, which is the mean of the perihelion distance PF_1 and the aphelion distance AF_1 in Fig. 4–5. Copernicus dimly sensed the law, which is reflected in the sidereal periods and relative radii of the simplified preliminary form of the Copernican theory; Kepler put it into precise mathematical form.

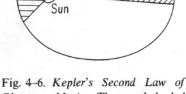

Fig. 4–6. *Kepler's Second Law of Planetary Motion.* The equal shaded areas are swept out in equal intervals of time.

7.5. Discovery of the Law of Equal Areas. Much of Kepler's early work on planetary orbits was directed to recasting the theory of Copernicus in order to simplify it and bring it into line with Tycho's data. Although his theory is called heliocentric, Copernicus had referred the motion of the earth and the other planets to a common center somewhat displaced from the sun. Kepler, however, referred all planetary positions to the sun itself.

To Tycho Brahe, Mars was a stumbling block. Its orbit has an eccentricity of 0.093, which is rather small but nevertheless 5.5 times greater than that of the earth and 15 times greater than that of Venus. At times Mars comes very close to the earth and becomes brighter than any planet except Venus. At other times, when near conjunctions with the sun, Mars is so far away that its brightness is little greater than that of the North Star. This large range of brightness made Mars a challenge to all early astronomers, whereas its relatively large orbital eccentricity made it difficult to describe the observed motion with Tycho's standards of accuracy, using only the mathematical tools Tycho had inherited.

During their brief period of collaboration Kepler worked with Tycho on the problem of Mars; he continued the research after the death of the older man. For a while he tried to work out a theory based solely on data obtained at times when Mars was in opposition to the sun. (At such times the direction of Mars as seen from the sun is the same as its direction as seen from the earth and can be determined with ease.) The method was only partially successful. Finally Kepler decided to redetermine the earth's orbit as a preliminary step to a fresh attack on Mars.

The procedure he followed in locating the orbit of the earth was a great improvement on any used before. It depended on the assumption — confirmed by the results — that in the Copernican frame of reference, fixed by the sun and stars, the planets traverse orbits that are *closed figures with fixed periods.*[9] It follows from this assumption that if any planet occupies a position M (Fig. 4–7) at any moment of time t_0 it will occupy the same position in the Copernican frame after an interval of one or more complete sidereal periods, or planetary years. Here is the crucial point of Kepler's method. Observations of a planet, Mars in particular, at intervals of one planetary year, show the directions of a fixed point in space observed from different points of the earth's orbit and can be used to determine the shape, relative size, and orientation of that orbit.

The method requires one to start with a moment t_0 when Mars is in opposition to the sun. The angle which the sight line from the sun through the earth to Mars makes with the vernal equinox at such a time can be measured and laid out on a chart like Fig. 4–7. On such a line two points are arbitrarily chosen to represent the positions of the sun and Mars, respectively. The distance between these points determines the scale of the map of the earth's orbit that is to be constructed.

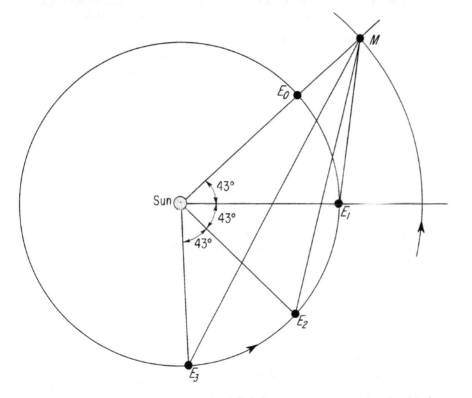

Fig. 4–7. *Kepler's Determination of the Orbit of the Earth.* Here M is a fixed point on the orbit of Mars observed at intervals of one Martian year. The series of observations begins when Mars is opposite the sun, so that the initial position of the earth, designated as E_0, is on the line joining the center of the sun with the point M.

After one Martian year (686.980 days) Mars should be back at M, but the earth will meanwhile have traveled through about 677°, lacking about 43° of two complete revolutions. Therefore, the earth will be at some such position as E_1 on the diagram. If one knows

[9] The sidereal period of each planet other than the earth is to be worked out from Eq. 4.2 or 4.3, as the case may be, using for S the accurately known mean value of the observed synodic periods. The variations in the observed synodic periods are due to the discrepancies between the actual motions of the planets and the approximation of uniform circular motion.

the directions of the sun and Mars as seen from earth, it is easy to lay out the corresponding sight lines and to locate the earth at their intersection. Further observations made at intervals of a Martian year serve to fix additional points E_2, E_3, $\cdots$ and so ultimately to determine the earth's orbit. The method can be checked by starting at a second point of opposition and verifying that a redetermination of the orbit gives the same curve.

Such is the procedure introduced by Kepler. He used only a few points and found, as he expected, that within his limits of accuracy the earth's orbit could be regarded as a circle. The center of the orbit (C in Fig. 4–8) was displaced from the center of the sun, however, so that the distance from the sun to the earth is not constant. It is a maximum at the aphelion point A on the same side of the sun as the center and a minimum at the perihelion point P on the other side of the sun. Moreover, the known variations in the speed of the sun's annual motion along the ecliptic could be correlated with the aphelion and perihelion points. It turned out that the apparent speed of the sun on the ecliptic is a minimum when the earth is at the aphelion point and a maximum when the earth is at the perihelion point. Clearly, this means that angle θ of the sightline from the sun to the earth must increase most rapidly when the earth is at P and least rapidly when the earth is at A.

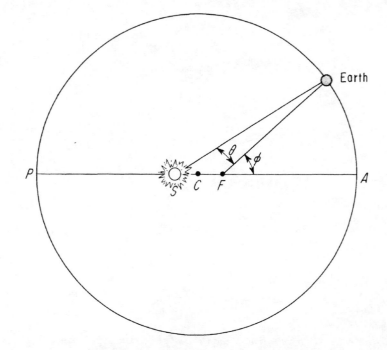

Fig. 4–8. *Kepler Uses Ptolemy's Equant for the Earth's Orbit.* In this diagram S is the sun, C is the center of the earth's orbit, and F is the equant point. The angle ϕ, measured at F, is assumed to increase uniformly with time, causing θ to change more rapidly when the earth is near the perihelion point P than when it is near the aphelion point A.

To account for the variations in the earth's angular velocity, Kepler reintroduced the equant conception of Ptolemy which Copernicus had rejected. He located an equant point F on the opposite side of the orbital center from the sun and at the same distance from the center as the sun. He assumed that the earth maintains a constant angular velocity with respect to F. From the geometry of our figure we see that Kepler's assumption gave the required minimum angular velocity about the sun when the earth is at aphelion and a corresponding maximum angular velocity when the earth is at perihelion. When checked against the observations, Ptolemy's equant proved to be quantitatively as well as qualitatively satisfactory.

Somewhat later he discovered that the equant rule could be replaced, within his limits of precision, by the assumption *that the radius vector from the sun to the earth sweeps out equal areas in equal intervals of time.* This new way of formulating the law of speeds pleased Kepler very much, for it transferred the seat of authority over the motion of the earth from the equant point, a point in empty space, to the sun. He belonged to the neoplatonic tradition and shared the mystical reverence of Copernicus for the sun, in which he saw the throne of God. At the same time he was enough of a modern to realize that the sun must dominate the earth and the other planets by some force that it radiates along with its life-giving stream of light and heat.[10]

Thus Kepler's second law, the law of equal areas, was uncovered in connection with the earth's orbit prior to the law of elliptic orbits (the first law). This was possible because elliptic orbits of low eccentricity are very nearly circular even when the distance of the center of the ellipse from either focus is appreciable. The earth's orbit is actually of this type; for it the eccentric circle, combined with either an equant or the rule of equal areas, works surprisingly well, although the same combination would be totally inadequate for an orbit of larger eccentricity.

When Kepler later discovered the elliptical form of the orbit of Mars, he was able to verify that the law of equal areas is correct in that case also. So, step by step, it has been checked as a universal law governing the motion of all satellites of the sun.

7.6. Discovery of Kepler's First Law. At this point Kepler should have had clear sailing in working out the orbit of Mars. The French mathematician Petrus Ramus had suggested some years earlier to Tycho Brahe that a new determination of the shapes of the planetary orbits relative to the sun was needed and that it should be independent of any such preconception as that of the eccentric circle and equant. The ideas involved in Kepler's determination of the earth's orbit could easily be used to work out the orbit of Mars as well. Once the position of the earth on the diagram of Fig. 4–7 at every moment of time was known, *any* pair of observations of Mars separated by an interval of one Martian year would give the directions of sight lines to a single point on the orbit of Mars from *known* points on the orbit of the earth. Figure 4–9 will serve to illustrate the procedure. By accumulating enough individual points the complete orbit can be defined.

Actually, Kepler seems to have worked out only a few positions of Mars by this method — sufficient to convince him that the orbit cannot be circular. But at this point, for reasons that are obscure, he turned to less straightforward procedures. For a time he worked

[10] Cf. G. Holton, *loc. cit.*

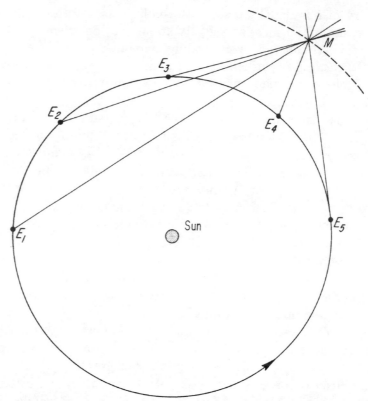

Fig. 4–9. *Kepler's Method for the Determination of the Orbit of Mars.* In this diagram the orbit of the earth is assumed known and *M* is *any* point on the orbit of Mars. The positions of Mars and the sun are observed at intervals of one Martian year.

on the assumption that the orbit is egg-shaped. Then, more or less by accident, he hit upon the assumption that the orbit is an ellipse with the sun at one of its foci. This assumption proved to fit Tycho's data for Mars very well. Later on it was successfully tested against the observations of the other planets and came to be known as Kepler's first law of planetary motion.

With this discovery the whole complicated machinery of epicycles that had disfigured the work of Copernicus could be eliminated. When referred to the sun-centered frame of reference, the orbits of all the planets turned out to be simple closed curves of the same type. At last the fundamental simplicity and harmony of the Copernican scheme was fully revealed. Here was clear proof of the superiority of the new conception of the solar system and a solid observational foundation for the future mechanical theory of Newton.

Unfortunately the discoveries received scant immediate attention. We read with sadness that even Kepler's contemporary and correspondent, Galileo Galilei, his companion-in-arms in the warfare against the authority of Ptolemy and Aristotle, never appreciated what Kepler had done. Kepler's works were tedious and difficult; his mysticism was alien to his Italian correspondent. Moreover, Galileo was preoccupied with his own discoveries in astronomy, with laying the foundations of a theory of motion, and with his lifelong warfare against Aristoteleanism.

Kepler's first two laws were published in 1609, about eight years after the death of Tycho Brahe. His third law, the one that sharpens up the relation between sidereal period and relative radius (which in a qualitative form had attracted the attention of Copernicus), did not appear for another 10 years. It was the third law that in another 50 years was to be the starting point of Newton's theory of gravitation.

With the publication of the third law the basic geometrical framework for the description of the solar system was complete.[11] Only details remained to be filled in, including the discovery of a few additional distant planets, the discovery of the asteroids, or minor planets, and the problem of absolute scale.

Figure 4–10[12] shows the orbits of the planets as far as Jupiter and those of a few well-known asteroids.

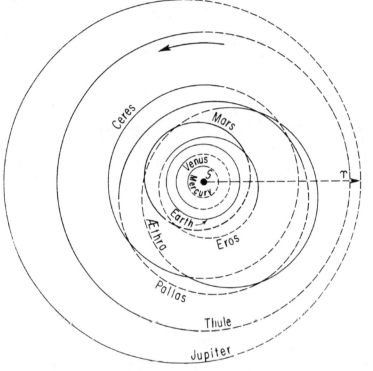

Fig. 4–10. *Map of the Inner Planetary Orbits.* This map shows to scale the orbits of the major planets from Mercury to Jupiter. It includes also the orbits of five of the more important minor planets, or asteroids, which are so small that they remained unobserved until the beginning of the nineteenth century. Nearly all members of this family have orbital diameters intermediate between those of Mars and Jupiter (cf. also Chap. 5, Sec. 2).

(This map reproduced with the permission of Blaisdell Publishing Company, a division of Ginn and Company.)

Exercise 4–1: Verify that, since the sun seems to rotate eastward relative to the celestial sphere, the counterclockwise direction of the earth's orbit in Fig. 4–1 is that which would be seen if the solar system were viewed from the pole of the ecliptic adjacent to the north celestial pole.

Exercise 4–2: The sun by May 21 of any year has moved away from the vernal equinox through an angle of 4 hours (30°) measured along the ecliptic; i.e., its celestial longitude is 4 hours. Locate the corresponding

---

[11] Once Kepler's laws were firmly established, the problem of determining the motion of any satellite of the sun was reduced to that of evaluating six parameters called the *elements* of the orbit. All six elements can be worked out from three or four separate photographs of the satellite against the background of stars taken at suitable intervals of time.

[12] After H. N. Russell, R. S. Dugan, and J. Q. Stewart, *Astronomy* (Ginn and Co., Boston, 1945), p. 236.

position of the earth in Fig. 4–1. Assuming that at the same time the celestial longitude of Venus is 6 hours, locate Venus on the diagram.

Exercise 4–3: The observed speed with which a planet moves along the ecliptic is of course variable. Therefore, the directly observed time required for the planet to make a complete circuit of the celestial sphere is not constant. Show, however, that (a) the *average* time required for an inferior planet to pass around the celestial sphere is equal to the earth's sidereal period (sidereal year), whereas (b) the average time required for a superior planet to pass around the celestial sphere is equal to its own sidereal period.

Index